WELL, LOOK AT THAT! HE TWISTED THEM IRON RAILINGS TO MAKE A HANDLE FOR HIS PAN!
HE SAID HE FANCIED A MEATY PANCAKE. BUT WHERE'S HE GONNA GET THE MEAT?
£1·60

D0236517

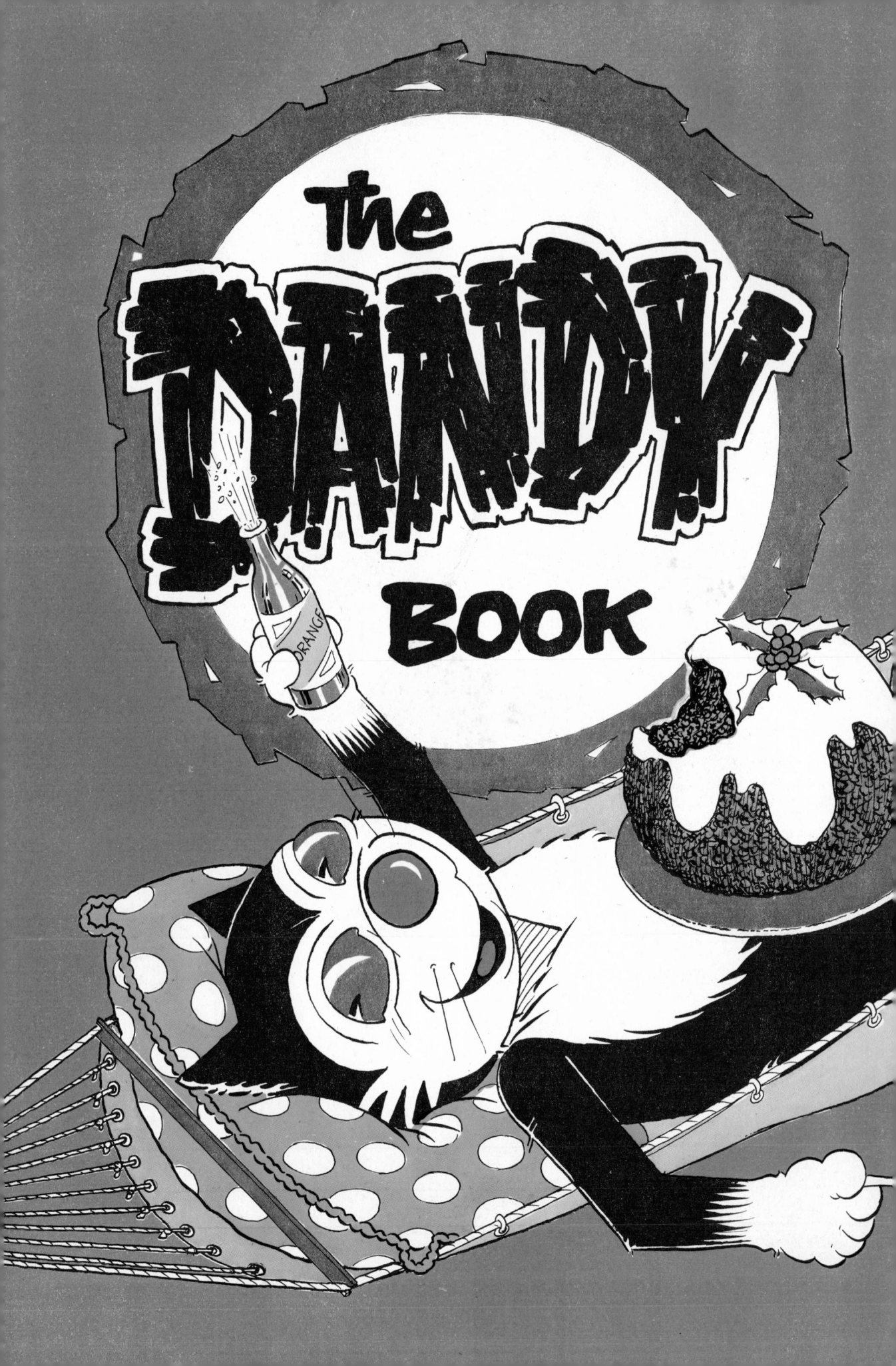
The
DANDY
BOOK
ORANGE

Printed and Published in Great Britain by D. C. THOMSON & CO., LTD., 185 Fleet Street, London EC4A 2HS
© D. C. THOMSON & CO., LTD., 1981.
ISBN 0 85116 200 2

TUFTY'S LUCKY TERRIER

TUFTY TOWNSEND braced himself in goal to face up to another darting raid from a remarkable footballer — one who had four legs, a tail and the name of Scamp.

Tufty was a new pupil at Brampton School and this was the day of the football trial match to pick the school team. So Tufty was putting in some extra practice with his terrier dog, Scamp, the wizard of the doggie dribble.

Leaving Scamp at home, Tufty dashed to the school playing fields where the Games Master selected the sides.
RIGHT! YOU PLAY IN THE STRIPED JERSEY TEAM, TOWNSEND.
Midway through the first half, Tufty missed a sitter.
OH, NO!
WHAT A MISS!
Then in the second half, he stumbled over the ball and bang went another scoring chance.
DRAT! I'VE TRIPPED MYSELF!
Next day, the chosen team was pinned up on the board. And Tufty's name wasn't listed!
HARD LUCK, TUFTY! YOU HAVEN'T BEEN PICKED!
Tufty was downcast as he ambled home at lunchtime. But he perked up when Scamp bounded to meet him. And the happy terrier gave Tufty a brainwave.
WE'LL GO AND WATCH THE GAME, SCAMP, AND YOU CAN BE OUR LUCKY MASCOT. I'LL DRESS YOU UP IN THE SCHOOL COLOURS.

The game had already started when Tufty and Scamp breezed up.
WHAT'S THE SCORE?
WE'RE ONE NIL DOWN!
NEVER MIND! SCAMP WILL SOON CHANGE OUR LUCK.
Before Tufty could stop him, Scamp scurried on to the pitch in excitement. And the left winger in the school team tripped over the terrier.
LOOK OUT!
YAHOO!
COME OFF THE PARK AT ONCE, SCAMP!
The winger had got such a nasty knock that a substitute had to be sent on.
KEEP THAT DOG UNDER CONTROL!
HIS LEG IS TOO BADLY BRUISED FOR HIM TO PLAY.
YOU'LL HAVE TO GO ON, SUTTON!
However, ten minutes later it was that very substitute, Sammy Sutton, who scored a great equaliser.
A GOAL!
HURRAH!

WHAT A SUPER GOAL!
And two minutes from the end of the match, substitute Sammy headed home a glorious winner.

The Brampton boys were over the moon at their success.
WE ARE THE CHAMPIONS!

Back at school, Tufty wanted to join in the celebrations, but he was due for a disappointment.
CAN'T I COME IN? AFTER ALL I BROUGHT ALONG THE LUCKY MASCOT.
SORRY, TOWNSEND! THE CELEBRATION IS FOR THE TEAM ONLY.

Suddenly a shout came from the next room. The trophy cabinet had been broken into.
SOMEONE HAS STOLEN ALL OUR SILVER CUPS!
SCHOOL TROPHY CASE

By now Tufty and Scamp were regarded as bringers of bad luck. They were both sent packing.
BUZZ OFF WITH YOUR POOCH!

Next day Tufty went to the golf course where trials were being held for the school golf team.
PUT MY NAME DOWN, SIR!
RIGHT, TOWNSEND! BE READY TO START IN HALF AN HOUR.

Tufty lined up for his first drive.

WHACK! The ball swerved away over the bushes.
FORE!
OH, DEAR! THAT DOESN'T LOOK TOO PROMISING!

There was a mighty crash as the ball struck the windscreen of a parked car.
WOW!

The Games Master snatched the club.
YOU'RE NO USE, TOWNSEND! FRED FENTON WILL GET THE LAST PLACE IN THE SCHOOL TEAM.

Although not chosen to play, Tufty decided to follow Fred round the course with lucky mascot Scamp. It wasn't long before Fred hit a stray shot.
THE BALL WENT INTO THIS LONG GRASS!
Fred couldn't find the ball at all.
IF YOU CAN'T FIND YOUR BALL, I WILL WIN THE HOLE!
YOU GO LOOK FOR IT, SCAMP!
Scamp went zig-zagging into the long grass hunting this way and that. Soon he gave a sharp bark of discovery.
LOOK! SCAMP'S FOUND IT!
Fred took careful aim and lofted a super shot out of the rough to end up inches from the pin.
WHACKO! SUPER SHOT!
The Brampton lad played inspired golf after that. He won the match that helped gain the cup for the school.
WELL PLAYED, FENTON!
AND WELL DONE SCAMP, TOO!
Once again Tufty asked if he might celebrate with the winners.
MAY I JOIN IN THE CELEBRATION? AFTER ALL, SCAMP BROUGHT US LUCK.
NO! IT'S FOR PLAYERS ONLY!

On the way home, Tufty was spotted by Slugger Sloan and other toughs from the school which Brampton had beaten in the football match.
THERE'S ONE OF THE ROTTERS FROM BRAMPTON. LET'S BASH HIM!
Slugger galloped after Tufty and grabbed him by the scruff of the neck.
HEY! LEGGO!
Writhing and struggling, the two lads battled it out. Then as Slugger forced Tufty to the ground, Scamp leapt to help his master.
Slugger lashed out at Scamp and knocked the terrier headlong over the edge and into a rugged quarry.
CLEAR OFF, YOU BRUTE!
Slugger's cruelty roused Tufty to a fury. He leapt up and landed a terrific punch on Slugger's jaw.
TAKE THAT, YOU BULLY!
Tufty's schoolmates arrived in time to see that wallop, and they chased off Slugger and his henchmen.
SCAMP! ARE YOU ALL RIGHT?

Scamp wagged his tail away down on the floor of the quarry and Tufty picked his way down towards him.
IT'S OKAY, LADS! I'LL SOON FETCH HIM UP.

The terrier was none the worse for his fall. He bounded to clamber back up the slope with his master.

Halfway up, Scamp paused. He had found the entrance to a cave half hidden by undergrowth.

Scamp scuttled inside and began barking loudly.
WHAT'S UP, SCAMP?

Mystified, Tufty crept warily into the gloom.
GOSH! IT'S DARK IN HERE!

What an amazing treasure trove met the boy's eyes!
LOOK, LADS! SCAMP HAS FOUND ALL THE TROPHIES THAT WERE STOLEN FROM THE SCHOOL!

All the silverware was accounted for, and the boys carried it to the top of the quarry.
YOUR DOG SCAMP HAS BROUGHT US LOTS OF LUCK THIS TIME, TUFTY!

Tufty's pals had been most impressed by the punch that had sent Slugger reeling, and they persuaded him to enter for the inter-school boxing championships.
HONEST, SIR, TOWNSEND HAS GOT A KILLER PUNCH!

When the day of the contest came Tufty climbed into the ring and found his opponent was none other than Slugger Sloan.
WELL, I'M BLOWED! I'M UP AGAINST SLUGGER!

Slugger had a score to settle and began to biff Tufty about the head.
OUCH!

As the fight swayed to and fro, Tufty got trapped in a corner and was taking a terrific battering from Slugger.
COME ON, TUFTY!
WHAT A BEAUTY!
All of a sudden Tufty heard Scamp bark from the ringside. That reminded him of Slugger's nastiness at the quarry, and in a surge of fury he swung a punch that almost knocked the bully's head off.
Slugger was counted out and Tufty was the champion.
EIGHT—NINE—TEN—OUT!
Tufty was presented with the cup. That one big punch made him the idol of the school. This time he could deservedly join in the celebrations, and so could Scamp, who had helped to bring everyone the best of luck.
THREE CHEERS FOR TUFTY TOWNSEND AND FOR SCAMP, TOO!

THE Smasher
IT'S THE NIGHT OF OUR CHRISTMAS BOXING TOURNAMENT. WE SHOULD DO VERY WELL!
BROWN STREET YOUTH CLUB
SLURP! LOOK AT THE PILE OF FOOD FOR AFTERWARDS!
BROWN ST. Y.C.
YEAH! BUT NONE OF YOU WILL BE IN A FIT STATE TO EAT IT!
ULP! THEY'RE SO BIG THEY'LL FLATTEN US!
BROWN ST. Y.C.
UNLESS...
COME AND DO SOME LAST MINUTE TRAINING —YOU LOOK AS IF YOU NEED IT!
WHY, YOU CHEEKY DOG!
GYMNASIUM
SWING
HO-HO! I'VE SWUNG THE DOOR ON 'EM!
BUMP!
BANG
BIFF!
GYMNASIUM
SWING
GURR! WE'LL GET YOU FOR THAT!
BROWN ST. Y.C.
I GIVE IN! HOW WOULD YOU LIKE SOME ASSAULTED NUTS?
YOU MEAN ASSORTED NUTS?
BROWN ST. Y.C.

NO! I MEAN ASSAULTED NUTS— YOURS!
BIFF!
BANG!
BONK!
HO-HO! THEY'RE HELPLESS NOW. QUICK— BALANCE THESE WEIGHTS ON THIS PUNCHBALL, LADS!
BROWN ST. Y.C.
TRAINING WEIGHTS
BONK!
BIFF!
BANG!
HO-HO! GOT 'EM AGAIN!
HA-HA!
RIGHT, CHAPS! TIME TO GET THE TOURNAMENT STARTED—EEK!
YOUR OPPONENTS ARE IN NO STATE TO BOX! THE TOURNAMENT MUST BE CANCELLED.
GROAN!
OO!
GREAT STUFF!
THE FIGHTS MAY BE CANCELLED, BUT THERE'S ONE THING THAT'S NOT—
THE GRUB!
MUNCH! CHOMP!
HURRAY! AND WE'VE GOT OUR OPPONENTS' HELPINGS, TOO!—ALL THANKS TO SMASHER!

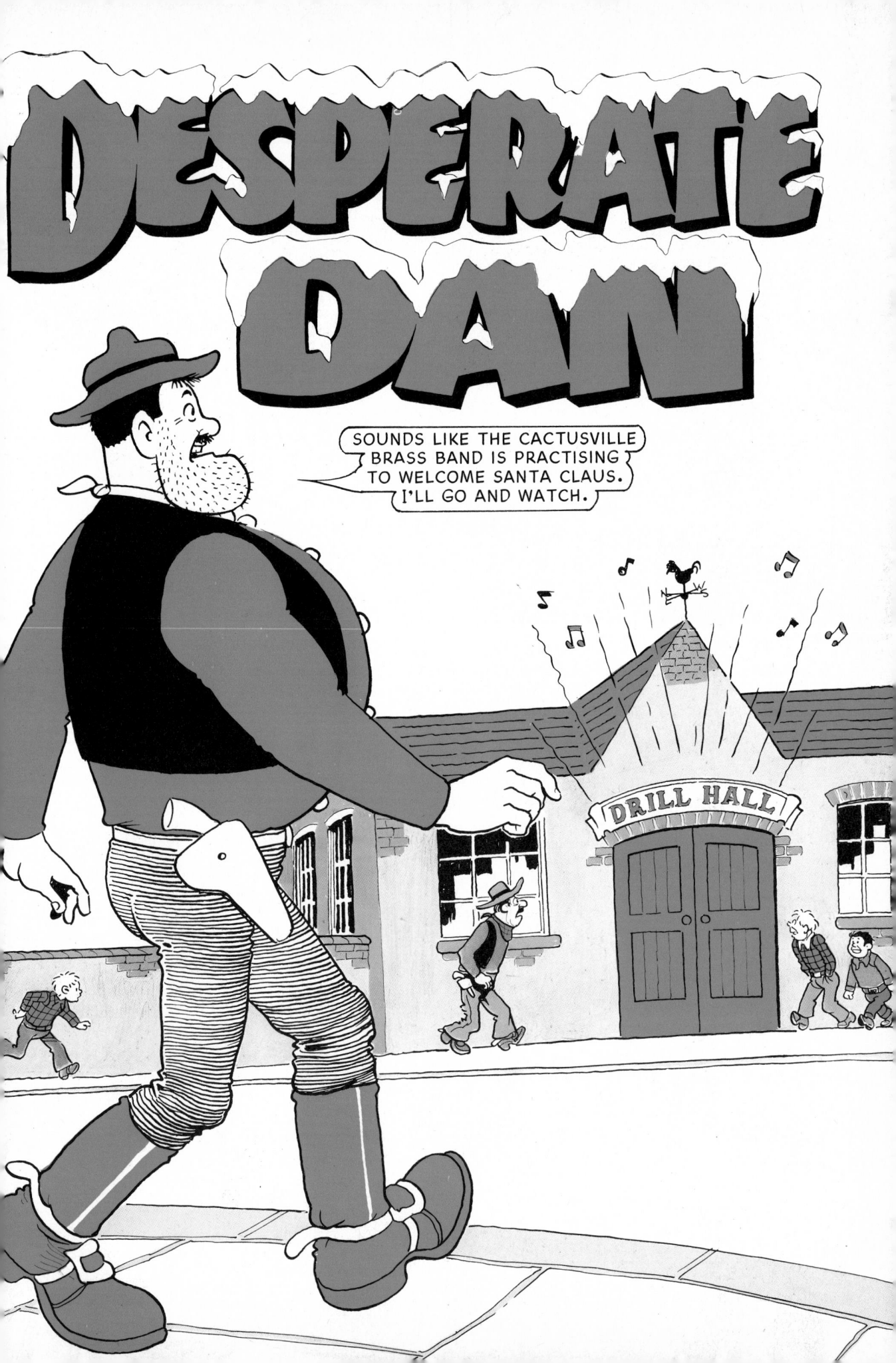
DESPERATE DAN
SOUNDS LIKE THE CACTUSVILLE BRASS BAND IS PRACTISING TO WELCOME SANTA CLAUS. I'LL GO AND WATCH.
DRILL HALL

SPARE A DIME FOR THE BRASS BAND'S CHRISTMAS FUND, DAN.
SURE!
WHOOPS!
THERE GOES MY LUCKY SILVER DOLLAR!
GOT IT!
SHRIEK!
STOMP!

ZUNK!
IT WOULD BE BAD LUCK TO LOSE THAT SILVER DOLLAR!
HELLO! WHAT'S HE JUMPING UP THERE FOR?
NOW LOOK WHAT YOU'VE DONE TO YOUR DRUM!
CRASH!

YOU BIG GALOOT! YOU'VE LAID OUT MY DRUMMER AND BUST HIS DRUM!
TAKE IT EASY, MISTER!
I'LL GET YOU A NEW DRUM AND A DRUMMER, TOO.

IN THE MUSIC SHOP—
A BIG DRUM, DAN? YOU MUST BE JOKING. THERE AIN'T NO SUCH THING AS A DRUM STRONG ENOUGH FOR YOU TO PLAY!
GEE! I CLEAN FORGOT THAT!

WHAT AM I GONNA DO? I'VE GOTTA GET A BIG DRUM SOMEHOW! SAY, THERE'S A PILLAR BOX! I WONDER—?
MUSIC

I'LL BORROW IT! GOOD JOB IT'S JUST BEEN EMPTIED.

I'LL NEED THE TOP OFF THIS OTHER BOX AS WELL.
RIP!
FIX THIS TOP ON TO THE BOTTOM OF THE FIRST BOX, AND JUST CRIMP DOWN THE EDGES.
THESE RAILINGS WILL MAKE FINE DRUMSTICKS. I CAN SQUEEZE THE TOP INTO A BALL.
IN THE DRILL HALL—
WHAT ON EARTH IS THAT AWFUL RACKET?
CLANG!
CLANG!
CLANG!
CLANG!
TWIRL!
HERE YOU ARE, MISTER! I TOLD YOU NOT TO WORRY— I'D GET YOU A NEW DRUM AND A DRUMMER TOO!
CLANG!
STOP! STOP!
YOU'LL BURST MY EAR DRUMS!

COME ON, YOU GUYS! STRIKE UP A TUNE!
ZUNK!

I CAN GIVE YOU A GOOD STRONG BEAT ON THE DRUM!

OH, NO!
WHANG!
WHUMP!
YEOW!

YOU STUPID BIG GALOOT, DAN! LOOK WHAT YOU'VE DONE TO MY BANDSMEN!
SORRY, MISTER! I GUESS I'M TOO STRONG FOR THIS DRUM!
IN ANY CASE A METAL DRUM IS NO USE. IT GIVES OUT THE WRONG NOTE. ONLY A WOODEN DRUM WITH ANIMAL SKINS PRODUCES THE RIGHT BOOM-BOOM!
ANIMAL SKINS, EH? BETTER BE A TOUGH ANIMAL IF I'M TO DO THE DRUMMING!
MUSEUM
HEY! LOOK AT DAN'S FUR COAT! HE MUST HAVE COME INTO A FORTUNE!
YIKE! WHAT'S HAPPENED TO THE GRIZZLY?
NATURAL HISTORY SECTION
GRIZZLY BEAR
BACK HOME –
IT WOULD BE A PITY TO SHAVE ALL THAT TOUGH HAIR OFF THE SKIN. I'LL JUST MAKE A HAIRY DRUM.

GROCER
SURE, YOU CAN HAVE IT, DAN. WHAT ARE YOU AIMIN' TO DO— CHURN YOUR OWN BUTTER?
HA-HA!
BEST BUTTER

IT'S BEGINNING TO LOOK LIKE A DRUM.
BEST BUTTER

ALL I HAVE TO DO NOW IS TIGHTEN UP THE CLAMPS.

BUT WHAT CAN I USE FOR DRUMSTICKS? IF I HIT THAT DRUM WITH ANYTHING I'LL BUST IT!

I NEED SOME SHOCK ABSORBERS— AND THE TOUGHEST ONES I KNOW ARE THE BUFFERS OFF A RAILWAY TRUCK.
RIP!

USE MY FISTS TO THUMP THE BUFFERS, AND THEY PREVENT THE DRUMSTICKS HITTING THE DRUM TOO HARD!
IT SOUNDS GREAT!
BOOM!
THUMP!
IN THE DRILL HALL –
SOUNDS AS THOUGH DAN'S FOUND A REAL DRUM SOMEWHERE!
BOOM!
BOOM!
BOOM!
BOOM!
WHAT ON EARTH IS THAT CONTRAPTION?
WHAT D'YOU THINK? IT'S A SUPER DRUM! LISTEN!
HOW'S THAT?
NOT BAD AT ALL!
HAW-HAW!
BOOM!
BOOM!
BOOM!

RIGHT! FORM UP! YOU FALL IN AT THE REAR WITH YOUR DRUM, DAN. QUICK, MARCH!
BOOM!
BOOM!
BOOM!
COUNTER MARCH, ABOUT TURN!
STOMP!
STOMP!
STOMP!

AW, GEE! NOT AGAIN!
BOOM!
STOMP!
OOF!
OOYAH!
YOW!
YOU GREAT, CLUMSY APE! YOU'VE LANDED ALL MY MEN IN HOSPITAL! WE'LL HAVE NO BAND FOR THE CHRISTMAS PARADE NOW!
IT WAS JUST A LITTLE ACCIDENT, MISTER! BUT I'LL FIX UP SOMETHING FOR THE PARADE.
AT THE HOSPITAL—
EVERY BANDSMAN WHO CAN BLOW A TRUMPET OR WHO CAN USE HIS FINGERS TO PLAY ONE IS NEEDED, DOC. THEY WON'T HAVE TO MARCH. I'LL DO THE MARCHING FOR THEM!
WARD
DOCTOR
WELL, YOU'D BETTER SEE THAT NO MORE HARM COMES TO THEM!

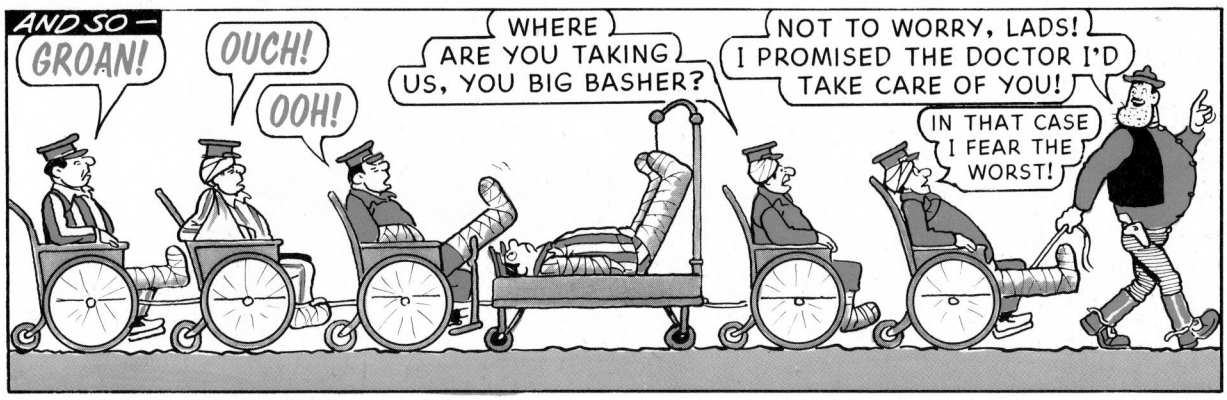
AND SO—
GROAN!
OUCH!
OOH!
WHERE ARE YOU TAKING US, YOU BIG BASHER?
NOT TO WORRY, LADS! I PROMISED THE DOCTOR I'D TAKE CARE OF YOU!
IN THAT CASE I FEAR THE WORST!

AT THE DRILL HALL—
THUD!
THUMP!
BANG!
THUD!
CLANG!
BANG!
CRASH!
THUMP!
WHAT'S ALL THE HAMMERING?
WHAT'S GOING ON IN THERE, ZEKE?
NO IDEA, PETE—BUT IT SOUNDS LIKE THEY'RE KNOCKING THE HALL DOWN!
DRILL HALL

THE CHRISTMAS DAY PARADE—
BLARE!
BOOM-BOOM!
BLARE!
BOOM-BOOM!
IT'S A FUNNY LOOKING BAND!
BUT IT CAN PLAY A GOOD TUNE!
IT'S SO LOUD! IT'S GONNA LIFT THE ROOFS WHEN IT GETS ALONG HERE!
SALOON
HOTEL

BLARE!
RAT-TAT!
RAT-TAT!
RAT-TAT!
RAT-TAT!
CLASH!

OOMPAH!
OOMPAH!
TOOT!
TOOT!
TOOT!
PARP!
PARP!

TOM TUM
HEE-HEE! I'VE SNAFFLED SOME GRUB FROM THE NEIGHBOUR'S PANTRY!
COME BACK, YOU PILFERING PEST!

Later, two joiners arrive—
I WANT YOU TO PUT AN EXTRA STRONG PADLOCK AND CHAIN ON MY PANTRY DOOR.
PANTRY

Presently—

TEE-HEE! NOW TO SNEAK INTO THE NEIGHBOUR'S HOUSE WHEN HE'S NOT LOOKING!

PANTRY
GOSH! THAT MAKES THINGS DIFFICULT— BUT I'VE GOT A PLAN!

GOOD! TOM TUM HAS GOT A BIG PIE. THAT SHOULD KEEP HIM HAPPY FOR A WHILE!

PANTRY
THIS IS A FAKE PIE! IT'S FULL OF WIRE-SNIPPERS AND OTHER TOOLS!

PANTRY
DONE IT!
SNIP!

OH, NO! HE'S EMPTIED MY PANTRY AGAIN!
TEAR!
TEAR!
YUM-YUM! THIS WILL MAKE A TASTY SNACK!
ZOOM!

KORKY the CAT
WHAT ON EARTH? THE WATER'S DEEP OUT THERE, AND YET KORKY'S STANDING ON IT!
NO FISHING
BUT HE CAN'T BE! HE MUST BE STANDING ON STILTS. I'LL SOON KNOCK HIM OFF THEM!
EEK! IT'S THE GAMEY IN A POWER BOAT. HE'S GOING TO RUN ME DOWN!
I'LL SWERVE AND BOWL KORKY OVER WITH A BIG WAVE!
I KNOW HOW TO DODGE THAT!
UP I GO!
PYONGG
SUFFERING SALMON! HOW DID HE MANAGE THAT?
Watch where you're going, Gamey!
THE ANSWER IS SIMPLE— I'M STANDING ON A TRAMPOLINE!
PYONGG
PYONGGG
YAHOO!
CRASH!

A SUPER "ICE"

WHAT'S BETTER THAN A *NICE ICE?* I'LL TELL YOU – IT'S A *NICE ICE TWICE!* LOOK NOW AND SEE HOW MANY *ICES* ARE IN THE WORDS IN THOSE FIRST TWO SENTENCES. NO LESS THAN FIVE! AND LOTS MORE COMMONPLACE WORDS CONTAIN *ICE.* HERE IN WORDS AND IN PICTURES ARE CLUES TO SOME OF THEM. SEE HOW MANY YOU CAN PUZZLE OUT BEFORE LOOKING UP THE ANSWERS *ON PAGE 141.*
1 THE GROCER PUTS THE HAM THROUGH THE _____
2 WHILE KORKY'S AWAY, WHO WILL PLAY? THE _____
SANDY BAY
3 THE GAMEKEEPER IS PUTTING UP A WARNING _____
NO FISHING
4 LOOK AT HIS BLACK MOUTH, AFTER HE'S BEEN EATING STICKY _____
5 THE SECRETARY WORKS IN A POSH _____
6 ARE LITTLE GIRLS REALLY MADE OF SUGAR AND _____?
7 A BIG CRACK IN THE GROUND IS A _____
8 THIS GLASS OF _____ REALLY HAS GOT ICE IN IT!
PURE ORANG

SCREAM from KORKY

The JOCKS and the GEORDIES

In a village on the Scottish Border are two schools, one on the Scottish side for the Jocks and another on the English side of the Border for the Geordies. When the two lots of schoolboys meet, there are always fireworks, like when they go to the waxworks—

WAXWORKS
AS A CHRISTMAS TREAT, BOYS, WE'RE PAYING A VISIT TO THE WAXWORKS.
HO-HO! WE COULD HAVE SOME FUN IN HERE!
ADMISSION 50p
Inside
HUH? IS THIS GEEZER LOOKING FOR OUR TICKETS?
HO-HO! HE'S ONLY A WAXWORK MAN. HE CAN'T DO US ANY HARM!
OH, NO?
PUSH!
AARGH!
OOF!

GOSH! THESE WAXWORKS CAN BE DANGEROUS THINGS! HO-HO!
TEE-HEE!
BAH! THE ROTTEN GEORDIES ARE HERE, TOO!
GURR!
DOH!

Later, in an old storeroom—
LOOK! THE HEAD COMES OFF EASILY!

42—43—44—
IT'S SMASHING FOR PLAYING HEADERS!
MY TURN NEXT!

OH-OH! HERE COME THE GEORDIES!
CHATTER
CHATTER

I KNOW HOW TO DEAL WITH THEM. WATCH THIS!

EEK! A HUMAN HEAD!
KICK!

BONK!
AARGH!
OOF!

HO-HO! LET'S GO!
WHAT ARE YOU BOYS PLAYING AT, SPRAWLING ALL OVER THE FLOOR? GET UP AT ONCE!
B-B-BUT—!

Presently—
KEEP YOUR EYES OPEN FOR THOSE GEORDIES. YOU NEVER KNOW WHAT THEY'LL TRY NEXT.
UMMF!

HEE-HEE! THE REST OF THE JOCKS WILL COME LOOKING FOR HIM!
THAT'S RIGHT! AND WE'LL TOPPLE A COUPLE OF HEAVY DUMMIES ON TOP OF THEM. LET'S GET THE DUMMIES INTO POSITION.

PHEW! THIS DUMMY OF HENRY THE EIGHTH IS A VERY HEAVY ONE!
WE'VE GOT EMPEROR NERO IN PLACE.

But—
LOOK AT THAT!
WE'LL SOON HAVE YOU FREE, BOY!
PUSH!
PUSH!
OUCH!
OOYAH!
GURR! THAT'S THE LAST STRAW! LET'S KNOCK SOME SENSE INTO THOSE SCHOOLBOY SCOUNDRELS!
Nearby—
JINGS! DID YOU HEAR THAT? THE TEACHERS WILL BIFF US IF THEY FIND US.
I KNOW WHAT TO DO.
ON
OFF

HEE-HEE!
I'VE SWITCHED OFF ALL THE LIGHTS.
CLICK!

DRAT! IT'S PITCH DARK, BUT THAT WON'T STOP US FINDING THEM!

WE CAN MAKE TWO CANDLES BY USING THE WHISKERS ON THIS WAX CAVALIER'S HEAD.
GOOD IDEA.

Soon—
SO THERE YOU ARE!
CRUMBS!
COME OUT AT ONCE!

A few minutes later—
FOUND YOU! COME OUT FROM BEHIND THOSE DUMMIES!
EEK! NOW WE'RE FOR IT!

WE'LL LOCK THEM IN THE CHAMBER OF HORRORS UNTIL WE FETCH A CANE.
JEEPERS!
CHAMBER OF HORRORS

I'LL STAND GUARD WHILE YOU GO FOR YOUR CANE!
OKAY!

YOU GO AND GET A CANE FOR YOURSELF IN CASE I BREAK THIS ONE ON THE BRATS!

AH, I SEE YOU'RE ALL READY FOR PUNISHMENT. I'M GOING TO WHACK THE DAYLIGHTS OUT OF YOU!

I'LL HANG THIS LIGHT UP HERE.
WHACK! WHACK!
OUCH! OUCH!
Minutes later—
WHAT'S THAT BURNING SMELL?
SNIFF! SNIFF!
BLISTERING BLACKBOARDS!
YOU'RE ON FIRE, BOY!
MOVE OUT OF THERE— HUH?
PULL!
EEK! WHAT'S HAPPENED TO HIS LEG?
SWOON!

QUICK! GRAB YOUR CLOBBER OFF THESE WAX DUMMIES AND WE'LL SCRAM OUT THE BACK WINDOW.
HEE-HEE! WE HAD OUR CLOTHES DRAPED OVER THE DUMMIES!

GRR! COME BACK HERE, YOU SCOUNDRELS!
HURRAH! WE'VE ESCAPED!
THAT WAS A SUPER WHEEZE!
HO-HO! THE TWO BIGGEST DUMMIES IN THE WHOLE PLACE ARE THE TEACHERS!

BERTIE BUNCLE
and his CHEMICAL UNCLE
HEY! DON'T BE A LITTER LOUT, BERTIE! DON'T THROW AWAY YOUR CHOCOLATE WRAPPER LIKE THAT. IT MAKES THE PLACE UNTIDY!
OOPS! SORRY, MUM!

DON'T WORRY, MUM! MY NEW INVENTION WILL SOON CLEAR THAT UP!
GOSH!
SUCK!

IT'S A VACUUM CLEANER DESIGNED FOR USE IN PARKS. IN FACT, IT'S GOING ON TEST IN OUR LOCAL PARK TODAY...
I'LL TAKE IT ALONG THERE FOR YOU, UNCLE BUNCLE.

HEE-HEE! I'LL GIVE IT A GOOD TEST BEFORE THE PARKS PEOPLE DO!
OOH! THESE NEW BOOTS ARE KILLING ME!
THROB!

HOI! WHAT'S GOING ON? WHAT'S THAT FUNNY MACHINE DOING?
SUCK!

GURR! COME BACK WITH MY BOOT!

I'D BETTER LET HIM GET HIS BOOT BACK...
I WONDER WHO'S IN CHARGE OF THIS THING?

WOW! IT'S OFF AGAIN BEFORE I COULD EXAMINE IT PROPERLY!

NOW I'LL HAVE A READ OF MY NEW DANDY!

ME FIRST, JIMMY! I'LL GIVE YOU IT BACK AFTER I'VE READ IT!
WOW!
SUCK!

THIS IS A CLOSE GAME WE'RE HAVING. WHO'S GOING TO WIN IN THE END?

ME! I WIN!
AARGH!
SUCK!
ERK!

GIVE US BACK OUR MARBLES, BUNCLE, YOU ROTTER!
PARK

GOTCHA! NOW GIVE US BACK THE MARBLES—OR WE'LL GIVE YOU THE WORST BASHING YOU'VE EVER HAD!
BIFF!
BASH!
OO! OKAY, OKAY!

FIRST I'LL HAVE TO FETCH THE MACHINE BACK.

HERE IT COMES. I'LL OPEN IT AND GIVE YOU BACK YOUR MARBLES.

HEY! WHAT'S THIS? IT'S STUFFED FULL TO THE BRIM WITH GOODIES!
HOI! THAT MACHINE SCOOPED UP ALL OUR PICNIC GRUB!

YUM-YUM! GOOD OLD BUNCLE! YOU CAN EVEN KEEP OUR MARBLES IF YOU LIKE!
COME BACK HERE, YOU RASCALS!
COME ON, LADS, RUN! WE CAN SHARE THE GOODIES OUT LATER!
WHIZZ!

Harry and his HIPPO
DAD DOESN'T WANT YOU IN THE HOUSE, HIPPO. HE SAYS YOU HAVE TO SLEEP OUTSIDE.
SHIVER!
CRASH!
SLAM!
Z Z Z Z
LEAP!
YIKE!
CRASH!
WHAT'S GOING ON? THE BRUTE'S BROKEN DOWN THE BACK DOOR AND WRECKED YOUR BED!
POOR OLD HIPPO! HE MUST HAVE BEEN FEELING THE COLD, DAD!
IF YOU BUILD A WARM KENNEL FOR HIM HE'LL BE ALL RIGHT OUTSIDE.
OKAY, I'LL BUILD ONE TOMORROW.
IT'S GOING TO BE BIG ENOUGH EVEN FOR HIPPO.
RIGHT, HIPPO! COME ON, IT'S TIME FOR BED.
GOODNIGHT, HARRY.

PUFF! I THINK I'LL NEED YOUR HELP TO GET HIPPO OUTSIDE. HE DOESN'T WANT TO GO!
HEAVE!
HEAVE!
PUSH!
HURRAY! WE'VE GOT HIM OUT!
SLAM!
IN YOU GO, HIPPO. IT'S WARM ENOUGH IN THERE.
OH, OH!
BAH! THE DOOR SLAMMED!
AND NONE OF US HAS A KEY!
IT'S ALL YOUR FAULT, HIPPO. COME OUT OF THAT KENNEL. WE'LL HAVE TO SLEEP IN IT TONIGHT!
SNORE!
SHIVER!
In the morning—
OH, NO! LOOK, DAD!
THAT BLINKING HIPPO HAS BURST HIS WAY INSIDE!
THE CUNNING RASCAL! HE'S THE ONLY ONE WHO GOT A WARM NIGHT'S SLEEP!
ZZZZZZZ

Desperate DAWG

I'LL SHOW YOU HOW TO BEND TWO BARS AT ONCE.
JEEPERS! HE'S BENDING THEM WITH ONLY HIS FINGERS!
TWEAK!
ALL RIGHT, CLEVER CLOGS! WATCH ME LIFT THIS HEAVY WEIGHT.
MAGNIFICENT! THAT WEIGHT HAS NEVER BEEN LIFTED BEFORE!
OHO! YOU GET THE JOB, DESPERATE DAWG!
HOW'S THIS THEN?
GURR! I'LL SHOW THAT WISE GUY!
BETTER START CLEANING UP ROUND HERE.
WHOOSH!
The bent bar spins like a boomerang . . .
CLUNK!
I THINK YOU MADE A WISE CHOICE, BOSS. YOU DON'T WANT A GUY WHO FALLS ASLEEP ON THE JOB! HEE-HEE!

JACK SILVER

ONE moment Curly Perkins was browsing quietly round a fantastic museum; the very next he was running like mad, for a huge Fuzzy Face with staring eyes had suddenly appeared in the doorway. It was probably the weirdest of all the weird animals Curly had encountered since he arrived here in the wacky world of Marsuvia, far off in Outer Space, on a visit to his Marsuvian pal, Jack Silver.

The stabbing prongs had an astonishing effect on the animal. As Jack leaped down to follow Curly, the Fuzzy Face puffed out its cheeks and blew.
ZAGH! IT'S BLASTING OUT CLOUDS OF SOOT!
GASP!

The choking soot filled the whole big room, and the boys didn't know which way to turn to escape. The soot cleared, but the monster had gone.
AND LOOK! ALL THESE GOLD STATUES AND THINGS HAVE GONE TOO, JACK!

The chums dashed out of the museum with the attendant, but there was no sign of the Fuzzy Face.
MUSEUM
THERE'S ZLOTTO AND HIS POOCHO! LET'S ASK IF HE SAW ANYTHING.

Jack told Zlotto what had happened, but the little chap was unable to help at all.
WHAT A FRIENDLY LITTLE POOCHO!
I SAW NOTHING COME OUT OF THE MUSEUM, JACK—AND MY POOCHO IS BLIND!

Jack and Curly were still chatting to Zlotto when a big van drew up beside them.
HEY, YOU, BOY! THAT POOCHO LOOKS AS IF IT CAN'T SEE!
THAT'S RIGHT. HE'S BLIND. SO WHAT?

The burly uniformed man snatched the old Poocho from its master.
ALL OLD AND USELESS PETS MUST BE PUT TO SLEEP. YOU KNOW THE LAW!
BUT HE'S NOT USELESS!

Curly Perkins decided he didn't like either this law or the man who was trying to enforce it. And he knew what to do about it!
YOU BIG BULLY! GO AND FETCH YOUR HAT!
HEY!

Quick as a flash, Curly snatched the Poocho's lead and ran for it. The queer dog was perhaps getting old, but it could still shake a leg!
COME BACK, YOU THIEVING RASCALS! I'LL CATCH YOU!
HO-HO! YOU'LL HAVE TO AIM YOUR LASSO GUN MORE CAREFULLY THAN THAT!

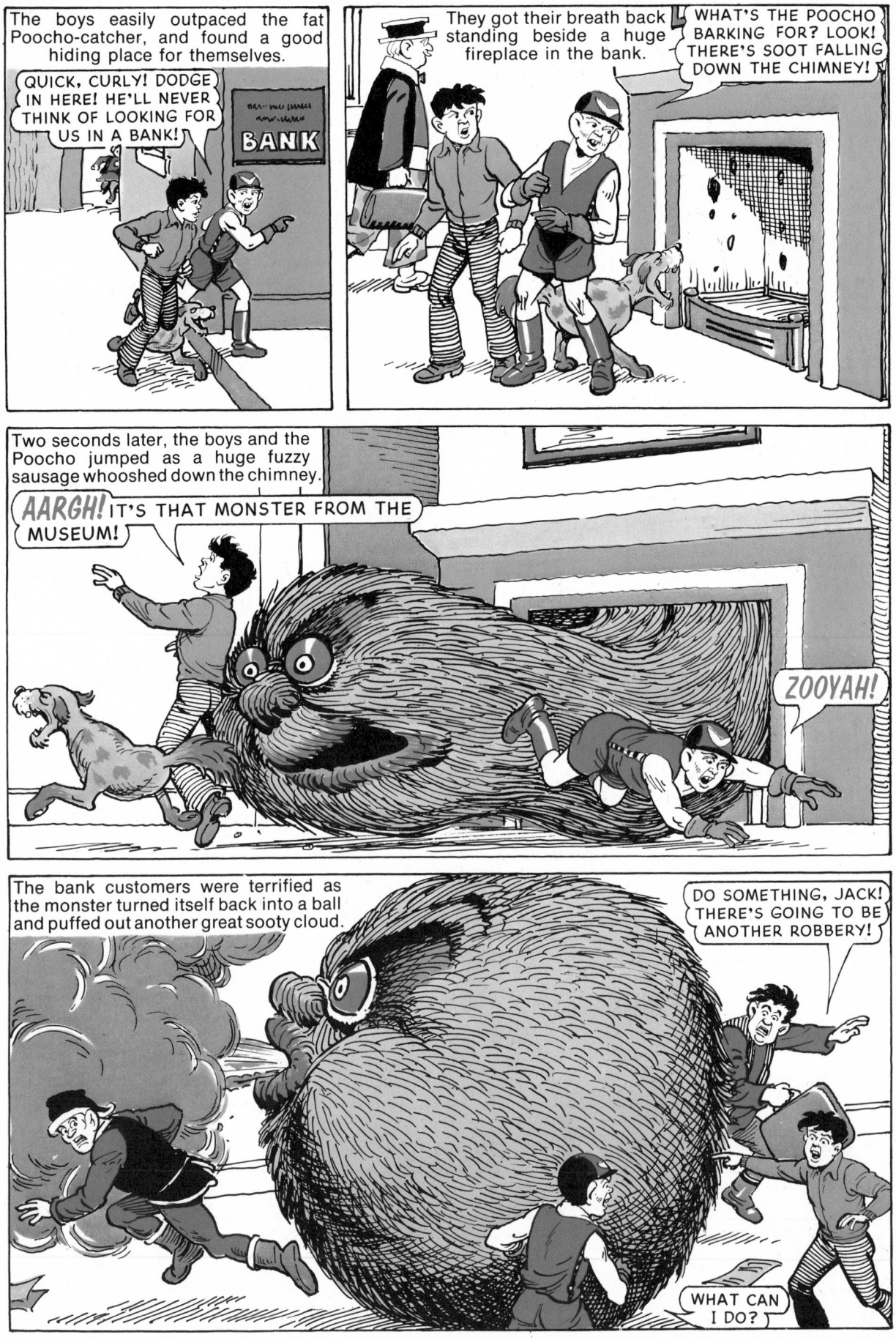
The boys easily outpaced the fat Poocho-catcher, and found a good hiding place for themselves.
QUICK, CURLY! DODGE IN HERE! HE'LL NEVER THINK OF LOOKING FOR US IN A BANK!
BANK
They got their breath back standing beside a huge fireplace in the bank.
WHAT'S THE POOCHO BARKING FOR? LOOK! THERE'S SOOT FALLING DOWN THE CHIMNEY!
Two seconds later, the boys and the Poocho jumped as a huge fuzzy sausage whooshed down the chimney.
AARGH! IT'S THAT MONSTER FROM THE MUSEUM!
ZOOYAH!
The bank customers were terrified as the monster turned itself back into a ball and puffed out another great sooty cloud.
DO SOMETHING, JACK! THERE'S GOING TO BE ANOTHER ROBBERY!
WHAT CAN I DO?

The sooty cloud billowed and swirled and engulfed the whole bank. Nobody could see a thing.
ZAIEE!
ZEEAGH!

The cloud cleared at last — and the boys saw at once that the robber had struck again.
ZOW! NOT A BANK NOTE LEFT! WE'VE BEEN CLEANED OUT!
ZASP! I GOT BIFFED!

Just then, the Poocho skipped up to Jack, drawn by the sound of his voice.
WHAT'S THAT YOU'VE GOT THERE, BOY? A PIECE OF BLUE CLOTH?
I BET IT COMES FROM THE ROBBER'S PANTS, JACK!

As Jack and Curly left the bank, they met a crowd of running people.
RUN FOR YOUR LIVES!
THE FUZZY FACE MUST HAVE STRUCK AGAIN, JACK!
IT'S HORRIBLE! ALL BLACK AND SOOTY!

The chums peered round the corner and what they saw made them gasp.
IT'S FLATTENING EVERYTHING IN THE STREET!

Suddenly the monster thumped down on to a moving car, then puffed out its cheeks and blew out yet another blast of soot.
WHAT'S THE IDEA? WHY HAS IT BLOWN A SOOT CLOUD ALONG THE STREET?

CRASH!
The answer to Jack's question was an almighty bang and the sound of splintering glass.
ZOWEE! LISTEN TO THAT! THE SOOTY CLOUD HAS CAUSED A TRAFFIC ACCIDENT!

Before Jack could do anything, the Poocho leaped forward into the thick cloud.
HEY! COME BACK! DON'T GO IN THERE!

The chums groped their way into the dense cloud to seek the blind Poocho.

When the sooty cloud began to clear, the boys saw that the street was jammed with wreckage. Several vehicles had piled into each other.
WE WERE CARRYING VALUABLE JEWELLERY. OUR VAN BURST OPEN IN THE CRASH AND WE DIDN'T EVEN SEE WHO ROBBED US!
SECURUM
GOSH!

But then the Poocho hopped up to Jack again.
ANOTHER SCRAP OF BLUE CLOTH! HOW DID YOU GET IT?
REMEMBER THAT HE'S BLIND! THE SOOTY CLOUD MAKES NO DIFFERENCE TO HIM!

Next moment, Jack spotted the Fuzzy Face up to more mischief.
LOOK! LET'S GET AFTER IT! COME ON, POOCHO!
MINT

Jack snapped out orders to the Poocho this time!
SEEK OUT THE ROBBER, POOCHO! SEEK!
GEMS

The blind Poocho dashed into the billowing and choking blackness.

Jack and Curly listened hard, and heard loud yells from inside the cloud.
ZAGH! NOT YOU AGAIN! GERROFF, YOU BRUTE!

Ten seconds later, the Poocho reappeared.
YOU'VE DONE IT AGAIN, POOCHO!
THE ROBBER WILL SOON HAVE NO PANTS LEFT!

The chums took the scraps of cloth along to the police station. Jack felt there was something familiar about them.
I'M SURE I KNOW WHO THE ROBBER IS—AND I THINK I KNOW HOW TO CATCH HIM!

BANK
And so, some time later a security guard left one of the city's banks with a gold shipment, accompanied only by Jack, Curly and the Poocho.
BE CAREFUL WITH THAT BULLION NOW!

It was asking for trouble, and trouble came along quickly — in the shape of the big Fuzzy Face.
LOOK OUT, JACK!
ZOW! I KNOW WHAT'S GOING TO HAPPEN NEXT!

Jack was right. The monster puffed out its cheeks and blasted a dense cloud around the bullion van.

But Jack Silver was ready this time!
QUICK! SWITCH ON NOW!

Whoosh! Out of the body of the gold trolley popped a powerful fan that blew the sooty cloud clean away.
WE CAN SEE WHAT'S HAPPENING NOW!
WHOOSH!
The vanishing cloud revealed the robber! It was Jack Silver's old enemy, Captain Zapp, the outlaw, wearing goggles that enabled him to see in the blackness.
HEY, YOU!
ZASP! I'VE BEEN TRICKED!
ZAH! THEY'LL NEVER CATCH ME!
Captain Zapp touched a switch and his jet-pack shot him into the air. But the Fuzzy Face was left behind, and Jack and Curly had come prepared. They fired a large net over it.
The monster went bouncing away, dragging the two boys.
DON'T LET GO, JACK! KEEP HOLD!
ZOWCH! MY KNEES!, BUT I CAN HANG ON!

The boys were scraped and bumped and banged along the ground, but they hung on grimly until they were dragged, panting for breath, into a woodland clearing.
LOOK! IT'S BROUGHT US TO WHERE CAPTAIN ZAPP'S SPACESHIP IS PARKED!
SO IT HAS!
Captain Zapp was loading up with the loot from his other robberies, but he whirled round when he heard his monster approaching.
YOU IDIOT! YOU'VE BETRAYED ME BY BRINGING ALONG THESE BRATS!
Wild with rage, Captain Zapp drew his blaster gun and fired.
GET THESE SPIES AWAY FROM HERE, YOU FUZZY FREAK!

But now it was the Fuzzy Face's turn to get angry. It huffed and it puffed and it blew Captain Zapp down with a monster soot cloud.
ZEEAGH!

Jack was scared that Captain Zapp would escape under cover of the cloud.
GO ON, POOCHO! SEIZE HIM!

Jack needn't have worried. When the sooty cloud cleared, the blind Poocho had its teeth sunk into Captain Zapp's leg, and the monster was bouncing up and down on him in a fury!
HO-HO! SERVES THE RASCAL RIGHT!
ZOOF! STOP! ZAIEE!

The monster at last gave up pounding the scoundrel and bounced off. But Captain Zapp was too dazed to resist arrest.
IT'S JAIL FOR YOU, BALDY!
AND WE'VE SEEN THE LAST OF THE FUZZY FACE. LOOK AT IT GO!

Every single piece of loot was recovered, and praises were heaped upon the gallant Poocho. But he was certainly in need of a bath after dashing in and out of so many clouds of soot!
ZAW-HAW! HE'S BEING PAMPERED LIKE A PRINCE!

Little Zlotto's Poocho had proved beyond doubt that it was still very far from useless. In fact, instead of having it put to sleep, the Mayor awarded it a special medal!
THANKS FOR SAVING MY POOCHO, JACK AND CURLY!
ZAW-HAW! IT'S CAPTAIN ZAPP YOU SHOULD THANK, BUT HE'S BEHIND BARS!

BULLY BEEF and CHIPS
HI-HO, SILVER! TWO-GUN CHIPS RIDES THE RANGE!
BEAT IT, BEEFY!
YOU'RE ON THE WRONG HORSE, CHIPS!
YAHOO!
THIS IS A BUCKING BRONCO—AND YOU'VE JUST BEEN BUCKED!
OOYAH!
SAY, PARDNER, IS THIS A TEN GALLON HAT!
OO!
DOESN'T SEEM TO HOLD TEN GALLONS.
GIVE ME MY HAT BACK!
MORE LIKE TWO GALLONS!
GLOOBLE!
I LIKE YOUR LASSO, CHIPS. IS THIS HOW IT WORKS?
BAH!

NOT A BAD THROW!
BUT I'LL HAUL THE LASSO IN AND TRY AGAIN.
WAH!
TUG
OUCH!
YOU'LL BETTER TAKE CARE, BEEFY. I'M AS QUICK ON THE DRAW AS ANY COWBOY!
PROVE IT!
I WILL—IF YOU DON'T LOOK FOR TWO MINUTES!
NO TRICKS NOW, CHIPS!
OH, NO! YOU'LL SEE I'M QUICK ON THE DRAW SHORTLY.
HERE YOU ARE, BEEFY! IN TWO MINUTES I'VE DRAWN SOMETHING THAT SMELLS LIKE A HERD OF BUFFALO!
SNARL!
NOW YOU'RE FOR IT!
CATCH ME THEN!
GURR! I SAW CHIPS DODGING BEHIND THAT TREE!
PULL!
WHACK!
OOYAH!
RIGHT ON TARGET!
COWBOYS ARE OFTEN CALLED COW-PUNCHERS, BEEFY. BUT I'M GOING TO BE A BEEFY-PUNCHER!
OO! GROAN!

TOM TUM
At Clarence Clutterbuck's house—
AND NOW CLARENCE WILL LET YOU HEAR SOME OF HIS FAVOURITE TAPE-RECORDINGS.
THIS IS A LOVELY PIECE OF BALLET MUSIC.
BAH! WHAT A LOAD OF SOPPY JUNK!
TRA-LA-LA!
PERHAPS YOU WOULD LIKE TO BORROW MY OLD TAPE-RECORDER? YOU'LL GET LOTS OF FUN FROM IT.
OH, ER! YES, THANKS!
Later—
ZOO
AH! I'VE GOT AN IDEA!
ROAR!
I'LL TAPE A LION'S ROAR.
MONKEYS
NOW TO VISIT THE MONKEY HOUSE.
HEE-HEE! JUST AS I HOPED. THAT ROAR HAS SCARED THE MONKEYS OUT OF THEIR WITS AND MADE THEM DROP THEIR BANANAS!
CLICK!
ROAR!
YUM-YUM! SUPER GRUB!
CHOMP!
MONKEYS

Next—
I'LL PLAY THE LION'S ROAR AT THE BIRD HOUSE.
POOP
SQUAWK!
HEE-HEE! THEY'VE FLOWN AWAY AND LEFT LOTS OF NUTS FOR ME TO GRAB!
CRUNCH!
MUNCH!
WHAT ARE YOU UP TO, YOU LITTLE HOOLIGAN?
CLEAR OFF!
A little later—
GOSH! THERE'S A NOISE I MUST TAPE!
AND THERE'S ANOTHER SOUND WORTH RECORDING.
Back at the Clutterbucks'—
I WANT YOU TO HEAR SOME OF MY FAVOURITE TAPES.
TRUMPET!
CHOMP!
SQUEAL!
TRUMPET!
HERE'S THE SOUND OF TWO ELEPHANTS FIGHTING OVER A BUN—
SLURP!
MUNCH!
DROOL!
SLURP!
AND THIS IS THE NOISE AT THE BIDDLECOMBE PIE-EATERS' CONTEST—
CRUNCH!
CRACKLE!
CRUNCH!
GRIND!
AND HERE'S A GORILLA CRACKING OPEN A COCONUT WITH ITS TEETH—
AND STAND BY FOR THE BEST ONE— ME EATING SAUSAGE AND CRISPS!
GOBBLE!
SLURP!
SNORT!
BURP!
OH, NO! HOW HORRIBLE!

Korky THE CAT
GOSH! THIS BOOK HAS GIVEN ME A WIZARD IDEA!
THE PIED PIPER of HAMELIN
MUSIC SHOP
I'VE BOUGHT A TOOTLER! IF THE PIED PIPER USED ONE TO LURE RATS ALONG, I COULD USE ONE ON MICE.
ALL KINDS of MUSICAL INSTRUMENTS
I'LL DO SOME PRACTISING!
TOOTLE-TOOT
MUSIC for BEGINNERS
But the mice have found Korky's book—
TOOTLE-OOO TOOT
SO THAT'S HIS GAME!
THE PIED PIPER of HAMELIN
I KNOW! LET'S MAKE HIM THINK HIS PLAN IS WORKING.
And so—
TOOTLE
HERE HE COMES, LADS— LET HIM HAVE IT!
OUCH! WOW! A BOMBARDMENT OF ROTTEN FRUIT!
WHIZZ
WHIZZZ
WHOOSH
HEE-HEE! WE FOOLED YOU GOOD AND PROPER!
HAW-HAW! EVER BEEN HAD, KORKY?
THAT'S WHAT YOU THINK! BUT I'VE FOOLED YOU. I'VE GOT THE LOT OF YOU OUT IN THE OPEN— WHERE I WANT YOU!
SLAM

TAKE THAT!
DRIED PEAS
SPRAY
OUCH!
PING
PING
EEK!
OOYAH!
AARGH!
PING
PING
PING
PING
PING
PING
PING
YIKE!
HA-HA!
I DIDN'T ONLY LEAD THEM OUT, I LAID THEM OUT AS WELL!
OW!
OOOH!
GROAN!
OUCH!
ZZZ

Peter's POCKET Grandpa
Ever seen a six-inch-tall lion tamer? That is the size of Peter Parker's Grandpa! And he has been that way ever since an angry gipsy used some strange power to shrink him down to midget size.
CRACK!
It was on the last day of school before the Christmas holidays that Grandpa became a "lion-tamer." Turn over and see how it happened.

HI, PETER! WHAT HAVE YOU BROUGHT HOME FROM SCHOOL IN THAT CARDBOARD BOX?
TELL YOU LATER, GRANDPA. I MUST SEE MUM FIRST.
PETER HAS PUT THE BOX IN THE GREENHOUSE. I'M GOING TO GET IN AND HAVE A LOOK.
I CAN'T GET THE LID OFF, BUT THIS KNIFE WILL OPEN THE BOX.
SOON SEE WHAT'S IN IT NOW!
EEK! A BIG WHITE RAT!
HELP! THERE ARE FOUR OF THEM! KEEP AWAY FROM ME!

PHEW! THEY'RE TAME RATS, THANK GOODNESS, AND THEY'RE ONLY INTERESTED IN ESCAPING!
I'LL HAVE TO RECAPTURE THEM BEFORE PETER FINDS OUT.
AH! THERE'S THE TAIL OF ONE OF THEM!
GOT YOU!
OH, NO! IT'S NOT ONE OF THE TAME WHITE ONES—IT'S A REAL LIVE, WILD ONE!
GOT TO ESCAPE! HELP!
OOPS! I'VE PULLED THE PLANT POT OVER!

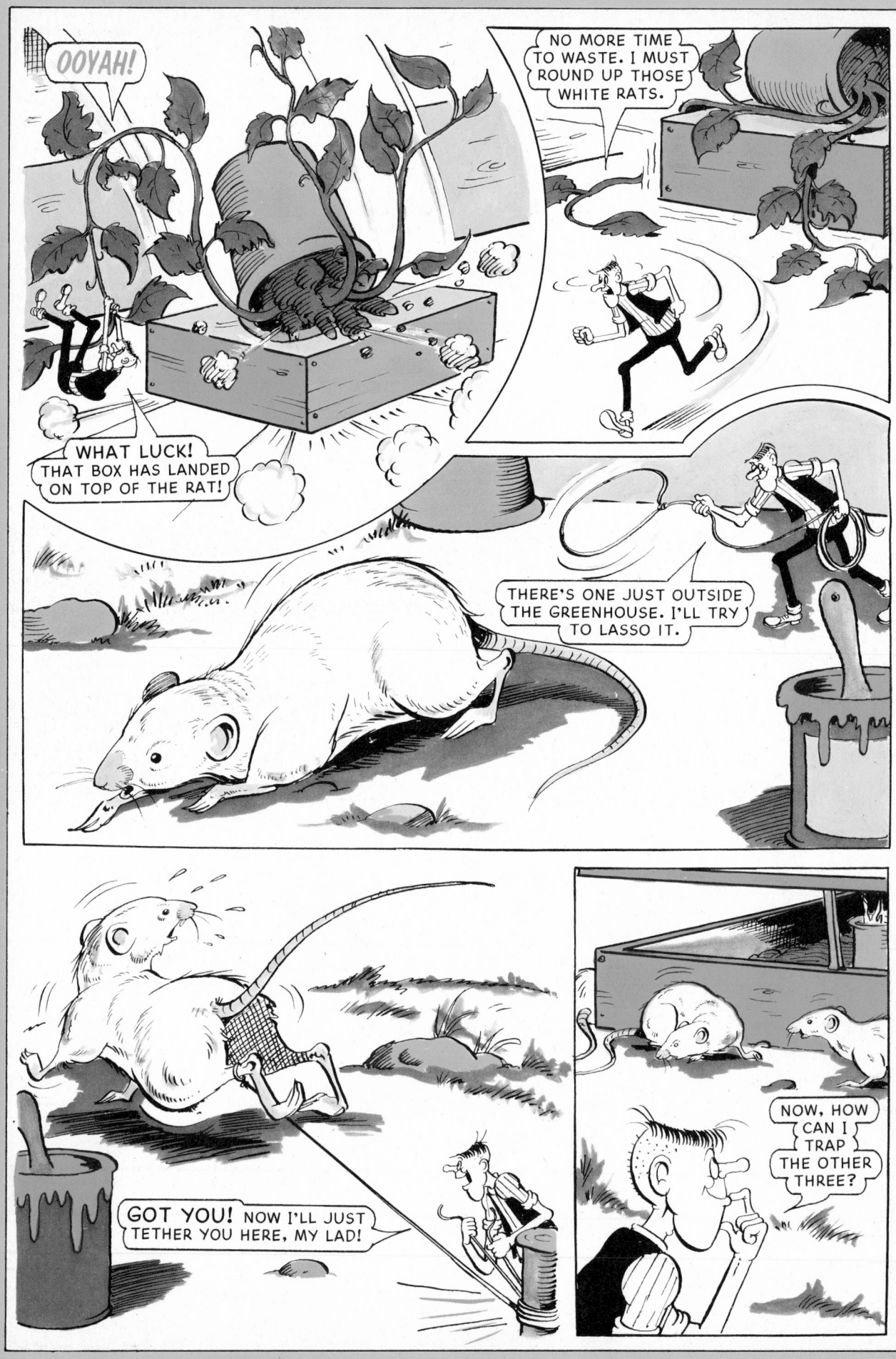
OOYAH!
WHAT LUCK! THAT BOX HAS LANDED ON TOP OF THE RAT!
NO MORE TIME TO WASTE. I MUST ROUND UP THOSE WHITE RATS.
THERE'S ONE JUST OUTSIDE THE GREENHOUSE. I'LL TRY TO LASSO IT.
GOT YOU! NOW I'LL JUST TETHER YOU HERE, MY LAD!
NOW, HOW CAN I TRAP THE OTHER THREE?

THESE BITS OF CHEESE I'VE BROUGHT OUT WILL MAYBE LURE THEM INTO DAD'S GARDEN FRAME.
IT'S WORKING! WATCH THIS!
JUST ONE GOOD SWIPE—!
SLAM!
CRACK!
AND THE LID DROPS DOWN AND TRAPS THEM. I CAN GO AND SEE PETER NOW!
OH, HELLO, GRANDPA. THAT BOX OF MINE HAS THE SCHOOL'S WHITE RATS IN IT. I'VE BEEN ASKED TO LOOK AFTER THEM DURING THE HOLIDAYS.
I—ER—FOUND THEM, PETER!
GRANDPA! WHAT A MESS!
OH, DEAR! THE STUPID ANIMAL HAS KNOCKED OVER AN OLD POT OF PAINT!

GOSH! YOU'VE TRAPPED THE RATS, BUT CRACKED ALL THE GLASS!
MY FRAME!
DAD'S GOING TO MAKE ME PAY FOR NEW GLASS, PETER—BUT I KNOW HOW TO GET MY MONEY BACK. LISTEN—
YOU'RE A CHEEKY SCAMP, GRANDPA! BUT IT MIGHT WORK!
WHISPER!
ROLL UP! ROLL UP! IT'S A GREAT SHOW FOR ONLY FIVE PENCE, PALS!
HOW D'YOU LIKE MY LION-TAMER'S OUTFIT?
HO-HO! THE "LIONS" ARE WHITE RATS!

CRACK!
HURRAY!
WHAT A TERRIFIC SHOW!
THERE YOU ARE, DAD. WE'VE MADE ENOUGH MONEY TO PAY FOR YOUR NEW GLASS!
HUMPH! WELL, I SUPPOSE YOU'VE DONE PRETTY WELL, YOU LITTLE RASCAL!

KORKY'S GALLERY

# of SCHOOLBOY HOWLERS

THE TRICKS OF
SCREWY DRIVER
PUT THE KETTLE ON, MUM. DAD'S HOME FROM WORK— AND HE'S FORGOTTEN HIS UMBRELLA AGAIN!
BLOOMIN' RAIN! I'M SOAKED THROUGH!
So—
I'VE INVENTED A NEW WET-WEATHER BOWLER FOR YOU, DAD.
I'M OFF TO WORK, SCREWY.
CRUMBS! A SPLASH OF WATER!
SPLOSH!
ULP! THE WATER'S TRIGGERED THE BROLLY MECHANISM!
HOI!
WHOOSH!
PAY UP FOR ALL THOSE CAKES.
GROAN! OKAY.
WALK WITH ME, SCREWY, IN CASE YOUR TRICKY BOWLER PLAYS MORE TRICKS!
At Dad's office—
HAND OVER THE WALLETS!
Whisper
A ROBBERY!
Whisper
WHAT ARE YOU DOING, SCREWY?
YOU'LL SEE!
THIS IS THE POLICE— STICK 'EM UP!
D-DON'T SHOOT!
JAB!
WELL DONE, THE DRIVERS! YOU'LL GET A NEW BROLLY AND A SLAP-UP FEED AS A REWARD!

GREEDY PIGG
WHAT LUCK! COOK HAS LEFT A BIG CUSTARD TART CLOSE TO THE WINDOW. I'LL HAVE IT!
HO-HO! THAT'S NOT A CUSTARD TART, IT'S A MUSTARD TART! I MADE IT SPECIALLY FOR PIGGY TO STEAL.
PIGGY'S GRABBED A TART FROM THE SCHOOL KITCHEN. THIS ROPE WILL HELP ME PINCH IT FROM HIM!
A CUSTARD TART! THANK YOU VERY MUCH, PIGGY!
ERK!
TUG!
LOOK WHAT JASPER'S GOT! C'MON, LADS, WE'LL FIX UP A LITTLE SURPRISE FOR HIM IN HIS WORKSHOP.
I CAN SCOFF THE TART IN PEACE IN HERE.
A PRESENT FOR ME! TA, JASPER!
CLUNK!
GURR! COME BACK, YOU YOUNG SCAMPS!
HURRAY! A BIG CUSTARD TART!

I'LL GIVE JASPER A REAL PASTING!
BAH! THE BUCKET'S WEDGED ON MY HEAD!
TAKE THAT!
AARGH!
BONK!
WHAT ARE YOU BOYS DOING WITH THAT TART? YOU KNOW YOU'RE NOT ALLOWED TO BRING TUCK INTO SCHOOL.
IT'S THE HEADMASTER!
BUT THIS IS A SPECIAL PRESENT TO YOU FROM THE COOK. WE WERE JUST ON OUR WAY TO GIVE IT TO YOU!
HOW NICE OF THE COOK! HE KNOWS HOW FOND I AM OF CUSTARD TARTS.
CHOMP!
AARGH! IT'S HOT!
YAH! YOWCH!
DID YOU ENJOY THE CUSTARD TART, PIGGY? I HOPE IT WASN'T TOO HOT FOR YOU!
TEE-HEE!
KITCHEN
TAKE THAT!
WHOMP!
YAHOO!
HEE-HEE! I DON'T KNOW WHY THE HEAD'S CHASING COOKIE, BUT I'M TOO BUSY EATING TO FIND OUT!
CHOMP! CHOMP!
OW! OUCH!

Bertie Buncle
nd his chemical uncle
FIRST I HAVE TO INSERT A TINY SIGNALLING GADGET INTO EACH BALL.
THAT'S CLEVER, UNCLE BUNCLE. YOU'VE EVEN INVENTED A SPECIAL TOOL TO GET IT INTO THE BALL!
'M FED UP LOSING GOLF BALLS OUT ON THE GOLF COURSE. THIS NEW MACHINE I'VE INVENTED WILL PUT AN END TO THAT!
GOSH! IT LOOKS LIKE A SPOTTED DOG, UNCLE!
HERE GOES FOR THE FIRST TEST. SEE! MY BALL HAS CURLED AWAY INTO THE BUSHES!
UT THERE GOES MY BALLSEEKER! LET'S FOLLOW HIM AND SEE HOW HE DOES.
SURE!
LOOK AT THAT! HE'S FOUND IT FIRST TIME!
BRILLIANT!
OH, BOY! I'LL SNEAK OFF WITH THE BALLSEEKER AND HAVE SOME SUPER FUN WITH IT!
LL JUST SLIP ONE OF UNCLE'S IGNALLING GOLF BALLS INTO TEACHER'S POCKET.
NOW TO STAND BACK AND WATCH THE FUN. THERE GOES THE BALLHOUND!

EEK! HELP! WHAT'S THIS THING? CALL IT OFF!
HO-HO! TEACHER'S RUNNING AND NOT LOOKING WHERE HE'S GOING!
OOYAH!
CRASH
CHUCKLE! THAT WAS GREAT FUN—AND IT'S EARNED ME A DAY OFF SCHOOL. TEACHER'S NOT FIT TO TEACH ANYONE.
I'LL HAVE A STROLL ON THE COMMON. AH! A CRICKET BALL!
I'LL THROW YOUR BALL BACK! AFTER I'VE STUCK ONE OF UNCLE'S GADGETS INTO IT!
HURRY UP, SON!
HERE'S YOUR BALL—AND THERE GOES THE BALLHOUND RIGHT BEHIND IT!
EEK! HELP!
IT'S GOING FOR MY ANKLES! OOYAH!
GURR I'LL DEAL WITH THAT THING!
SNAP
SNAP!! SNAP
GET OUT OF HERE!
YEOW!
GOSH! EITHER MY HOUND HAS GONE HAYWIRE—OR MY NEPHEW THINKS HE'S A GOLF BALL!
AARGH! OOYAH! GET THIS SNAPPER OFF MY NOSE! YOWCH!

DESPERATE DAN
THE CIRCUS IS COMING TO TOWN, AUNT AGGIE. I'M GOING OUT TO SEE THE PROCESSION THROUGH THE STREETS.
WELL, DON'T BE LONG, DAN. YOUR COWPIE IS IN THE OVEN AND IT'S NEARLY READY.
YEAH! I CAN SMELL IT! BUT DON'T YOU WORRY. I DON'T AIM TO LET IT SPOIL!
THE CIRCUS COMES TO TOWN

GREAT! I'M DEAD NUTS ON CIRCUS SHOWS!
CIRCUS
BOOM
BOOM
But in the lion's travelling cage—
SNIFF
SNIFF
SNIFF
GRAND CIRCUS
AND
MENAGERIE
LOOK OUT!
SHRIEK!
SUFFERIN' SNAKES! I'M A GONER!

AFTER HIM, DAN! HE JUMPED OVER THE FENCE INTO YOUR GARDEN.
DID HE NOW? WELL, I'LL JUMP OVER AND NAB HIM!

NO PESKY LION IS GONNA PLAY AROUND IN MY GARDEN!
LEAP!

AIN'T NO SIGN OF HIM IN THE FRONT GARDEN.

DOGGONE IT! NO SIGN OF HIM IN THE BACK GARDEN EITHER. HE MUST HAVE JUMPED THE FENCE!
WHIZZ!
I'LL JUST HAVE TO JUMP IT, TOO, AND TRACK HIM DOWN.

Out on the prairie—
NARY A SIGN OF THE CRITTER! HE'S VANISHED! WELL, I'M GETTIN' PECKISH, SO THE CIRCUS MEN WILL HAVE TO TRACK THE BRUTE ON THEIR OWN. I'M OFF HOME FOR MY COWPIE.

OH, THERE YOU ARE, UNCLE DAN! COME QUICK! AUNT AGGIE IS YELLING BLUE MURDER FROM THE HOUSE! MAYBE THAT LION'S IN THERE!
WHA-A-AT?
DAN! WHERE HAVE YOU BEEN? THERE'S AN ESCAPED LION IN HERE! COME AND THROW HIM OUT AT ONCE!
COMING, AUNT AGGIE! I SEE HOW THE BRUTE GOT IN!
YOU BRUTE! YOU ROTTEN GREEDY BRUTE!
GET AWAY FROM THERE! THAT'S MY COWPIE!
THIS'LL TEACH YOU NEVER TO SCOFF MY COWPIE AGAIN, MY LAD! BACK TO THE CIRCUS YOU GO!
WHACK! WHACK!
HOWL!

TOSS
AND DON'T YOU DARE BREAK OUT OF THERE AGAIN!
CRASH!
Back home—
THERE'S NOT MUCH LEFT TO EAT NOW, I'M AFRAID, DAN.
BUT I'M STARVING, AUNT AGGIE! PROMISE YOU'LL COOK AN EXTRA BIG COWPIE TOMORROW!
OH, ALL RIGHT! I PROMISE!
Next day—
OH, WHAT A SUPER SMELL OF COWPIE! I AIN'T GOING OUT TILL I'VE EATEN IT!
SNIFF SNIFF
But Dan's not the only one to smell it!
SNIFF SNIFF
SNIFF
LOOK, BOSS! THE LION'S BROKEN OUT OF THAT EXTRA STRONG CAGE WE PUT HIM IN!
MUST BE THAT COWPIE HE ATE. MAYBE IT MADE HIM EXTRA STRONG! ROUND UP THE MEN AND GET AFTER HIM!
Meanwhile—
THERE AIN'T GONNA BE NO INTERRUPTIONS THIS TIME!
EXTRA LARGE COW-PIE
EXTRA STRONG MUSTARD

SHRIEK! DAN!
IT'S THAT LION AGAIN!
DAN!
WHERE IS HE?
DON'T TRY TO TACKLE HIM, AUNT AGGIE!
SNIFF
CRASH!
DEAD FAINT
KEEP AWAY, AUNT AGGIE! LEAVE HIM TO ME!
OH, NO, YOU DON'T!
SPLATT!

OUT YOU GO, YOU GREEDY PEST!
OH, DO BE CAREFUL, DAN.
BOOT

AND NOW I'LL GRAB YOU AND GIVE YOU SUCH A LEATHERING!

DRAT! HE DODGED ME!

HO, THERE YOU ARE! WELL, JUST YOU WAIT!

I'LL JAM YOUR GREEDY HEAD IN THIS BUCKET, THEN TIE YOU UP UNTIL I'VE EATEN MY COWPIE!

HOLD STILL, YOU SNEAKY TWISTER!

WELL, LOOK AT THAT!
HE'S BITTEN THROUGH THE WIRE!
SNAP
TWANG

PYONG
PYONG
WHAT'S THE STUPID BRUTE'S IDEA? HE'S BITING THROUGH ALL THE WIRES!
SNAP
TWANG

PUSH!
RUMBLE
RUMBLE
WELL, I'M BLOWED! HE GOT ME TIED UP IN BARBED WIRE, AND NOW HE'S TRYING TO RUN ME DOWN!

THE CUNNING BRUTE! THOUGHT HE WOULD FLATTEN ME WITH MY OWN BIKE! JUST WAIT TILL I GET AT HIM!
RUMBLE

GOT TO GET RID OF ALL THIS DRATTED BARBED WIRE FIRST.
TWANG
TWANG
MY TEETH ARE AS GOOD AS ANY LION'S! THAT'S GOT RID OF THE LAST BIT.
BITE
GOBBLE
MUNCH
MY BIKE WILL GET ME BACK TO THE KITCHEN QUICK!
BUT NOT QUICK ENOUGH!
CRUNCH
MUNCH
AT IT AGAIN, ARE YOU? I'VE A GOOD MIND TO SKIN YOU ALIVE!
SPLATT!

I GOTTA FIND A WAY OF KEEPIN' YOU AWAY FROM MY COWPIE— AND I THINK I KNOW HOW!
THIS SHIP'S ANCHOR CHAIN IS JUST THE THING!
GRAND CIRCUS
CLANK
CLANG
WHAT'S DAN DOING WITH OUR LION?
SEARCH ME!
A HUGE LENGTH OF RAILWAY LINE DRIVEN DEEP INTO THE GROUND! BUT WHY DIDN'T YOU PUT HIM BACK INTO HIS CAGE, DAN?
THUMP
HE ESCAPED FROM HIS CAGE, DIDN'T HE? WELL, HE WON'T ESCAPE FROM THAT!
ZZZ
I SURE HOPE YOU'RE RIGHT, DAN!

WHAT'S UP, DAN? DO YOU WANT THAT CAGE TO PUT HIM IN IF HE ESCAPES AGAIN?
WELL, MAYBE!
CIRCUS
NOW WHAT ON EARTH DOES HE WANT TO BORROW A CAGE FOR?
Next day—
LOOK AT THAT LION! HE'S GOT WIND OF SOMETHING!
BET HE SMELLS COWPIE AGAIN. BUT DON'T WORRY, BOSS. HE WON'T BREAK THAT ANCHOR CHAIN.
LOOK! HE'S BENDING THAT LENGTH OF RAILWAY LINE!
SNIFF
STRAIN
HE'S DONE IT! HE'S GETTING AWAY! STOP HIM!
YOU MUST BE JOKING!

FOOLED YOU THIS TIME, GREEDY FACE! MAYBE YOU CAN BREAK OUT OF A CAGE, BUT YOU CAN'T BREAK INTO THIS ONE—NOT WHEN I'M INSIDE IT!
CIRCUS
COW PIE
(EXTRA LARGE)

IZZY SKINT
HE ALWAYS IS!
DARTS
IT'S NO FUN WALKING ROUND A FAIRGROUND WHEN YOU'RE SKINT, SAM.
YOU'RE RIGHT, IZZY!
PERFORMING DOGS! THAT GIVES ME A GOOD IDEA.
ENTRY 50p
MARVO AND HIS PERFORMING DOGS
IF I COULD TEACH OUR BONGO TO PERFORM TRICKS, PEOPLE MIGHT PAY ME TO COME AND SEE HIM!
I DOUBT IT VERY MUCH!
I'LL START TRAINING BONGO RIGHT AWAY.
C'MON, BOY! I WANT YOU TO JUMP THROUGH THIS HOOP.
HURRY UP, BONGO. JUMP THROUGH THE HOOP— BAH! HE'S NOT BUDGING!
THAT BONE MIGHT MAKE BONGO CHANGE HIS MIND.
HE'LL JUMP THROUGH THE HOOP TO GET AT THE BONE.
HERE, BONGO, A JUICY BONE FOR YOU!

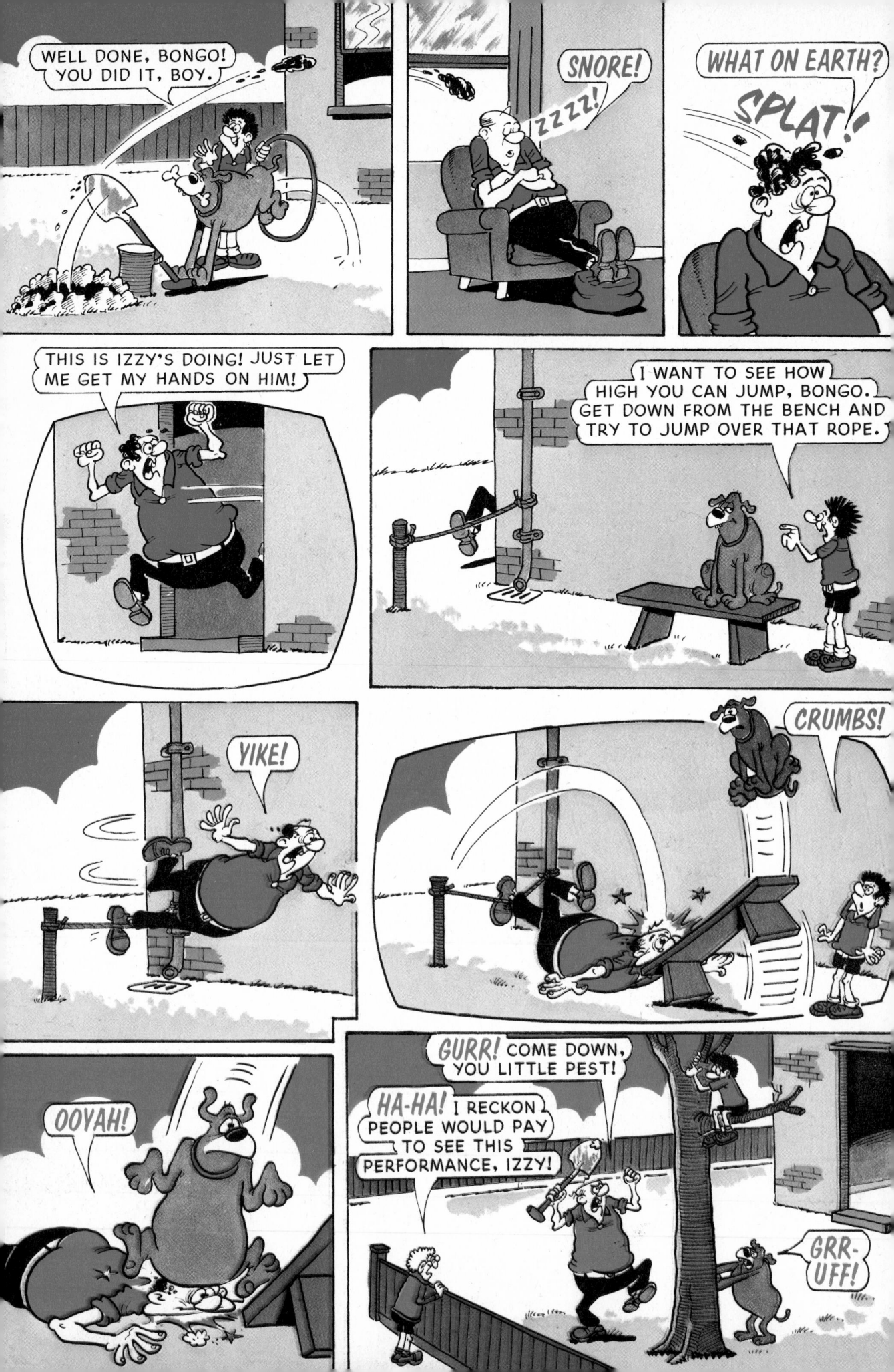
WELL DONE, BONGO! YOU DID IT, BOY.
SNORE!
ZZZZ!
WHAT ON EARTH?
SPLAT!
THIS IS IZZY'S DOING! JUST LET ME GET MY HANDS ON HIM!
I WANT TO SEE HOW HIGH YOU CAN JUMP, BONGO. GET DOWN FROM THE BENCH AND TRY TO JUMP OVER THAT ROPE.
YIKE!
CRUMBS!
OOYAH!
GURR! COME DOWN, YOU LITTLE PEST!
HA-HA! I RECKON PEOPLE WOULD PAY TO SEE THIS PERFORMANCE, IZZY!
GRR-UFF!

THE SMASHER
I'M STARVING, SO I'LL "BORROW" SOME BISCUITS.
BISCUITS
OH-OH!
BISCUITS
OOF!
CRASH!
WHAT WAS THAT NOISE? IS THAT YOU, SMASHER?
MUM SOUNDS ANGRY! I'M OFF!
I'LL TRY SNEAKING SOME GRUB FROM THE PANTRY.
SHOVE
SWING
OOPS! NO WONDER I'M CALLED SMASHER!
BUMP!
SMASH!
GURR! WAS THAT YOU TRYING TO STEAL SOME FOOD?
ME, MUM? MUST HAVE BEEN THE WIND!
GROAN! I'M STILL HUNGRY!
HEY, SMASHER! HOW ABOUT US PLAYING COPS AND ROBBERS?
OKAY, BILLY.
YOU GO INTO MY HOUSE, FILL A BASKET WITH GRUB—AND I'LL BE THE COP.
ER . . .
SHOVE
I HOPE SMASHER'S MUM DOESN'T CATCH ME ROBBING THIS "BANK"!
STOP, ROBBER!
WHAT'S THAT? A ROBBER?
GOOD LAD, SMASHER!
GRAB!
WELL DONE, SON! YOU DESERVE SOME GRUB AS A REWARD!
THANKS, DAD.
COME HERE, YOU LITTLE THIEF!
MUNCH! CHOMP!
HUH! CRAFTY OLD SMASHER! NOW I KNOW WHY HE LET ME BE THE ROBBER!

HERE'S A HOOT!

WHAT'S FUNNY ABOUT A *BOWL* WITH AN *OWL* IN IT? NOTHING MAYBE—EXCEPT THAT THERE ARE TWO *OWLS* IN THAT FIRST SENTENCE. THERE'S ONE IN THAT WORD *BOWL*, YOU SEE!
AND IT'S SURPRISING HOW MANY OTHER WORDS HAVE AN *OWL* IN THEM. SEE FOR YOURSELF WHEN YOU TRY THIS GAME. EVERY PICTURE GIVES A CLUE TO A WORD WITH AN *OWL* IN IT. PUZZLE THEM OUT AND DON'T LOOK UP THE ANSWERS (*ON PAGE 141*) UNTIL YOU'VE FOUND THEM ALL.

1
MIDNIGHT _____

2
A PAINTER USES A _____ TO REMOVE PAINT.

3
THE APPLE PIE IS SITTING ON THE WINDOW_____

4
A _____ OF SOIL.

5
A TORTOISE WALKS VERY _____

6
"HOWZAT?" SHOUTS THE _____
CLICK

7
IN SCOTLAND SOME PEOPLE VISIT THE HIGHLANDS AND SOME VISIT THE _____

SPOT THE "OWL"!

8
HE HAS A _____ ON HIS FACE!

9
THESE TWO CARS ARE FIXED TOGETHER BY A _____

10
A ____ OF FRUIT.

11
IF I STICK A PIN IN HIS PANTS, THAT WILL MAKE HIM ____

12
THE SHAPE OF THIS COWBOY'S LEGS.

13
THE SOUND A WOLF MAKES.

14
FOUND IN THE FARMYARD.

15
A HAT WORN BY A CITY GENT.

16
THEY'RE PLAYING A GAME OF _____

17
THE ARCHER HAS MISSED THE TARGET VERY _____
TWANG!

18
WHO INVENTED FRACTIONS, BOY?
HENRY THE EIGHTH, SIR.
AN EXAMPLE OF A SCHOOLBOY _____

19
YOU'LL LEARN A LOT FROM THIS BOOK OF _____
ENCYCLOPEDIA

20
DON'T ANNOY THE DOG OR HE'LL _____
GRRRR

BRASSNECK

CHARLEY BRAND was the lad with the most amazing pal in the world. Brassneck was an all-metal boy, with cog and spring innards and an electric brainbox. He could walk and talk and do all the things any boy could do — and lots more besides. He could even ride a horse and make it go like the wind. Read on and see how it all happened.

Brassneck's tremendous adventure began on the day when Dad Brand took the whole family to a country fair. Brassneck and Charley had great fun and Mum and Dad, too, enjoyed it no end.
WOULDN'T MIND WINNING A LIVE PIG OR A BARREL OF CIDER! I'LL TAKE A TICKET IN BRASSNECK'S NAME. HE'S GOT LOADS OF LUCK!
METAL PEST! CAN'T YOU MISS JUST ONCE?
COCONU
MERRY-GO-
SHOOTIN ALLERY
GRAND RAFFLE
SUPER LIST OF PRIZES
LOOK AT BRASSNECK, MUM! HE'S A DEAD SHOT.

At the end of the day they went home on the bus as happy as larks, with large ice creams and an armful of coconuts.
SHOULDN'T WE HAVE STAYED FOR THE RAFFLE DRAW, DAD?
NO NEED! IF BRASSNECK WINS, THE PRIZE WILL BE DELIVERED.
KISS M QUICK
I LOVE ME
I LOVE LUDO

They were sitting at their supper when there came a knock at the door.
MAYBE SOMEBODY'S COME TO DELIVER MY PRIZE!
HO-HO! WHAT AN OPTIMIST YOU ARE, BRASSNECK!

But it was indeed a man from the fair, and he wanted to know if Brassneck Brand lived at this address.
WHY, YES, HE DOES.
GOOD. HE'S WON A SUPER PRIZE. HERE, GRAB THIS ROPE!

Dad was left blinking at the rope in his hands.
WHAT KIND OF A PRIZE IS THIS?
He gave the rope a tug, and next moment a very large head poked its way round the door.
EEK!
A HORSE!
He wasn't the most handsome horse in the world, but one person fell in love with him at first sight.
THAT UGLY BRUTE WILL GO RIGHT BACK TO THE FAIR!
NO, HE WON'T! THIS IS MY HORSE! NOT YOURS!
But Dad was just as determined and furious, too!
GET RID OF IT, I TELL YOU!
LOOK WHAT YOU'VE DONE! MADE ME HIT THE HORSE!
The indignant horse whirled around and hoofed Brassneck in the midriff.
BLEEK!
HOI! WATCH IT!

And that kick knocked Brassneck's works wonky. He would not listen to Dad's commands or to Charley's pleading. He would keep that horse, come what may!
I'LL TETHER LIGHTNING HERE IN THE GARDEN FOR THE NIGHT. AND I'LL GUARD HIM AND BASH ANYONE WHO DARES TO TOUCH HIM!
GROAN!
BRASSNECK'S GONE BATTY!
There was nothing else for it but to go to bed. Charley awoke early in the morning and looked anxiously out.
YAWN—OH, GOOD GRIEF! MR CRUMP'S GARDEN!
Greedy Lightning had eaten everything in the Brands' garden, then chewed his way through the hedge and cropped as much as he could reach of all that grew in the neighbour's garden.
AARGH! MY APPLE TREE! EATEN BARE!
It was more than Mr Crump could take. He rushed indoors and snatched up the first weapon he saw — a big frying pan.
GET OUT OF HERE, YOU MONSTER!
But as Mr Crump's pan crashed down, Brassneck's head popped up. CLANG!
LEAVE MY LIGHTNING ALONE, YOU BIG BULLY!
CLANG!

Dad surveyed the damage to his neighbour's property. His own garden looked as though ten million caterpillars had held a banquet there!
WHERE HAVE YOU BEEN? WHY HAVEN'T YOU BEEN HERE MAKING SURE THAT FOUR-LEGGED MINCER DIDN'T MINCE UP EVERYTHING THAT GROWS?
I WAS AWAY GETTING LIGHTNING SOME FOOD!
ER... YOU DROPPED YOUR HAT, MR CRUMP.

Off rushed Brassneck, to return moments later carrying half a haystack from round the corner.
SEE! I BROUGHT ENOUGH TO KEEP LIGHTNING GOING.
HURRY UP, YOU FOOL, BEFORE HE EATS THE JERSEY OFF MY BACK!

Next thing an angry farmer appeared. It seems he had followed the trail of hay all the way from his farm.
THAT HAY WAS TAKEN WITHOUT PERMISSION— SO PAY UP!
YOU'VE DONE IT NOW, BRASSNECK!
I DON'T CARE! LIGHTNING IS HUNGRY!

And, of course, Mr Crump wanted payment for his damaged garden.
IF THIS KEEPS UP, I'LL BE BROKE INSIDE TEN MINUTES!

Now Dad had definitely had enough.
GET A SCREWDRIVER AND PUT BRASSNECK TO RIGHTS AT ONCE, CHARLEY. HE MUST GET RID OF THAT HORSE.
I WON'T! I'VE ENTERED LIGHTNING FOR THE MIDTOWN STEEPLECHASE ON SATURDAY!
Dad Brand scoffed at the very thought.
THAT STOMACH ON FOUR LEGS—A STEEPLECHASER? DON'T MAKE ME LAUGH!
I'LL SHOW YOU!
Brassneck leapt on Lightning's back, and prodded him in the flanks.
STOP!
GIDDUP, LIGHTNING!
DON'T BE DAFT, BRASSNECK!
HUP—AND OVER!
Lightning bounded forward, and his leap carried him crashing through the top of the hedge into the garden of the Brands' other neighbour. Mr Hopper got a fearful fright as the horse thudded into his fish pond!
EEK!

Mr Hopper raved angrily at Dad Brand.
THAT FOUR-LEGGED BULLDOZER HAS DESTROYED MY FISH POND!
HE HASN'T, HAS HE?
The hoofs had gone clean through the plastic bottom and all the water had drained away.
LOOK AT IT! YOU CAN BUY ME A NEW ONE, BRAND!
GROAN!
THIS IS YOUR FAULT, BRASSNECK!
But Brassneck wasn't listening! Spurred on by him, Lightning tried to clear Mr Hopper's gate — but couldn't jump high enough and bashed it down.
C'MON, LIGHTNING, WE'RE LEAVING!
EEK!
THERE GOES MY GATE NOW!
GIDDUP, LIGHTNING!
Out into the country and over fields and farmyards galloped Lightning. No gate could stop him — he simply blundered straight through them!

For the next few days Brassneck kept his horse in hiding and the crafty metal lad made a muzzle for him to keep his appetite in check. Brassneck figured that Lightning was too heavy with food to be able to jump.

Charley tracked Brassneck down eventually by following the trail of broken gates and flattened fences.
ONE BLADE OF GRASS AT A TIME, LIGHTNING.
YOU'LL NEVER MAKE A JUMPER OF HIM, BRASSNECK.

But Brassneck had a surprise in store for Charley. He had spent lots of time teaching Lightning to jump.
I'VE GOT HIM GOING! WATCH THIS!

Then Brassneck leaped on to Lightning's back.
AND SEE? HE REALLY HAS LEARNED HOW TO CLEAR A FENCE!

By the end of the day Brassneck had Lightning leaping like a grasshopper all over the countryside.
HUP, LIGHTNING! GOOD BOY!
GREAT JUMP! BUT IS HE FAST ENOUGH TO RUN A RACE?

By Saturday morning Brassneck had thought up a way of ensuring that Lightning ran like lightning. He paid an early morning visit to the Brand house.
I'VE PINCHED THESE EGGS. NOW ALL I NEED IS SOME MILK...
The bucketful was for Lightning! Brassneck broke the eggs into the milk while Lightning drooled.
THIS WILL BUILD UP YOUR STRENGTH FOR THE RACE, BOY!
The hungry horse dipped into the bucket and slurped like mad.
TUCK IN, LIGHTNING! THIS IS GOOD HORSE FOOD!
He licked up the last drop and rolled an eye at Brassneck. He wanted more!
NO—NO MORE, LIGHTNING! NOT UNTIL AFTER THE RACE!
Just then, Mrs Brand appeared at the door. It was time to scarper!
GO, LIGHTNING! HUP, BOY!
BRASSNECK! COME BACK HERE! WHAT HAVE YOU DONE WITH ALL OUR MILK?
The now lean and hungry horse cleared the front gate with plenty room to spare!

Brassneck persuaded Charley to bring another bucketful of milk and eggs along to the Midtown racetrack and give Lightning a whiff of it.
THAT'S FOR YOU, BOY— AT THE END OF THE RACE!
Now Brassneck turned the horse and rode him all the way round the track to the starting gates, with Lightning looking back longingly at the bucket.
I'LL TAKE YOUR MUZZLE OFF SOON, LIGHTNING.
In fact, that was the last thing Brassneck did before remounting at the starting gates.
HURRY UP! YOU'RE HOLDING UP THE RACE!
The gates were opened. And they were off! And the eager Lightning bolted into the lead like a shot from a gun!
Lightning cleared the first fence ahead of every other horse.
GO, BOY—GO!

Never had anyone seen a horse race so fast! The other jockeys saw only his clean pair of heels all the way round the track.
GASP! THAT ONE'S GOING LIKE STEAM!

GO GET IT, BOY!
The winning post! Lightning streaked towards it with his eyes fixed upon the bucket beyond it. Crafty Brassneck had known how to make the horse live up to his name!
WHAT A HORSE!
COME ON, LIGHTNING! HERE'S YOUR GRUB!

And that's how Brassneck and Lightning won the Midtown Steeplechase.
NOW YOU'LL COME HOME, BRASSNECK, WON'T YOU?

But that's not the end of the tale. You see, although Dad had no love for Lightning, Mum certainly had, and she had risked a whole pound on him.
RESULTS
1 LIGHTNING 100/1
2 FERRY BOY 7/2
3 JUNIOR JIM 3/1
GRACIOUS ME! IT'S LIGHTNING! I'VE WON A HUNDRED POUNDS!

Brassneck and Lightning were made very welcome back home — especially by Dad!
I ALWAYS SAID HE WAS A CHAMPION HORSE!
While Charley repaired Brassneck's upset works, Dad Brand cleared out the garden shed.
I'M TURNING THE SHED INTO A STABLE FOR LIGHTNING.
That night there was a smashing party in the Brand household. The winnings had paid for all the damage and left plenty over to buy loads of party fare. And Dad sang all the horsey songs he knew.
A FOUR-LEGGED FRIEND!
YES, A FOUR-LEGGED FRIEND!
OIL
But next morning, when Dad looked out the window . . .
GOOD GRIEF!
Lightning had done it again! During the night he had broken out of his stable and crashed through the fence into the next garden. There he had eaten all the choicest fruit and vegetables — and he was still at it!
BRAND! COME OUT HERE! LOOK WHAT YOUR NAG HAS DONE!

Cruncher Caine, the champion wrestler, was the owner. Poor Dad didn't dare argue with him.
THAT HORSE IS A BLOOMIN' WRECKER! IT HAS GOT TO GO!
Y-Y-YES, MR CAINE!
In spite of the joy Lightning had brought them yesterday, the whole Brand family realised that it was just not possible to keep a horse in their back garden — and especially not one with Lightning's appetite.
TAKE IT EASY, BRASSNECK. WE REALLY CAN'T KEEP YOUR HORSE.
Lightning was sold that same day, and Brassneck and Charley made fond farewells to the world's hungriest horse while Dad counted the loot.
OO! WHAT A LOT OF MONEY!
WE'LL LOOK AFTER HIM VERY WELL—AND YOU CAN ALWAYS VISIT LIGHTNING.
GOODBYE, OLD CHUM!
The money from the sale paid for all the damage. And it also bought Mum a new rig-out, Dad a barrel of cider, and Charley a bucket of ice cream. As for Brassneck, the retired jockey could now afford to dress like a lord every day of the week!
YOU'RE THE BEST AND LUCKIEST PAL I EVER HAD, BRASSNECK!
ICE CREAM

Bully Beef and CHIPS
FAMOUS POETS
WORDSWORTH
KEATS
LONGFELLOW
COLERIDGE
BURNS
ELLIOT
THOMAS
NOW THAT ENDS THE POETRY LESSON. I WANT YOU TO GO HOME TONIGHT AND WRITE A LITTLE VERSE ON ANYTHING YOU SEE.
SO, IN THE PARK—
"I SAW THREE SHIPS GO GLIDING BY, SAILING IN A BREEZE..."
"THEN CHIPS SANK BENEATH THE WAVES! NOW WASN'T THAT A WHEEZE?"
SPLOSH!
EEK! MY BOAT!
BAH! YOU'VE SUNK OUR BOATS, YOU ROTTEN BULLY!
HO-HO! TOO BAD!
LATER—
"'TWAS ON A SUMMER EVENING, A PIGEON CAME TO CALL—"
SPLAT!
YAAGH!
L—EGGS—YOGHURT
"IT LAID AN EGG UPON CHIPS' HEAD, HIS JACKET, SHORTS AN' ALL!"
MILK
BEEFY!
HEY, SONNY! DID YOU SEE WHO PINCHED AN EGG FROM HERE?
ILK
YES!
DAIRIES
AND I'LL MAKE HIM PAY FOR IT!
STILL LATER—
"A DUSTMAN WENT UPON HIS ROUNDS, AN EMPTYING OF THE BINS..."

UGH!
PROD!
"A BIG ONE DID ON CHIPS TIP OUT ITS TEA LEAVES AND KIPPER SKINS!"
WHAT ON EARTH?
IF I FIND OUT WHO DID THAT...!
I CAN TELL YOU WHO DID THAT!
NOW, CHIPS—LET'S HEAR YOUR POEM!
ER...WELL, UM...ERM...
CLUMP! SNARL!
CLUMP! SNARL!
AAH!—"HARK! I HEAR HEAVY FOOTSTEPS, I SEE BEEFY'S ANGRY DAD!"
YOU LITTLE VANDAL! I'VE A BILL HERE FOR THREE MODEL SAIL-BOATS—AND AN EGG! AND I GOT A BLACK EYE FROM A DUSTMAN! I'M GOING TO TEACH YOU A LESSON!
D-DAD!
THIS IS JUST FOR STARTERS—
—"WHAM! BLAT! BIFF AND THUMP! HE BELTS HIS IDIOT LAD!"
WHACK!
WHACK!
WAH!
"NOW BEEFY, HE HAS BEEN WELL TAUGHT, BUT AT BULLYING HE'S A LOSER. AND THAT'S THE END OF MY LITTLE TALE, A COMIC VERSE FOR YOU, SIR!"
HO-HO!
BEST VERSE I'VE HEARD! TOP OF THE CLASS, CHIPS!
GROAN!

Greedy PIGG
OH, DEAR! THE COOK'S ILL AND CAN'T COME IN TO COOK THE LUNCH TODAY. WHAT CAN WE DO?
I'M A FINE COOK, HEADMASTER. I CAN FIX UP LUNCH FOR THE BOYS.
THAT'S VERY HELPFUL OF YOU, MR PIGG.
I'M COOK TODAY, BOYS. I HOPE YOU ENJOY MY COOKING.
BAH! WHAT TINY HELPINGS!
NOT ENOUGH TO FEED A MOUSE!
OOK, JASPER! PIGGY'S LOCKED HIMSELF IN THE KITCHEN TO SCOFF ALL THE GRUB WE SHOULD HAVE GOT FOR LUNCH!
THAT TABLE HAS METAL CASTERS. I KNOW HOW TO MAKE USE OF THEM!
I'M RIGHT UNDER WHERE PIGGY IS AND THIS STRONG MAGNET WILL PLAY TRICKS WITH HIS TABLE!
I'LL START WITH THE PIE.
ERK!
THE TABLE MUST HAVE ROLLED DOWN A SLOPE ON THE FLOOR! I'LL MOVE MY STOOL OVER THERE.

ERK! THE TABLE'S MOVED AGAIN!

SCHOOL KITCHEN
I'LL GET A HAMMER AND NAIL THE TABLE DOWN TO STOP IT ROLLING.

HERE HE COMES NOW, LADS!
THAT'S ENOUGH POLISH, PERCY. I'LL PUT THE MAT DOWN AGAIN.
POLISH

I'D BETTER HURRY BEFORE ANYONE SEES ALL MY GRUB AND SCOFFS THE LOT!

WHAT ON EARTH? I'M SLIPPING!

GOT HIM! NOW I'LL SLAM THE DOOR.
WHOOSH!

HEE-HEE! THAT'S PIGGY SAFELY LOCKED AWAY!

BAH! LET ME OUT OF HERE!
BROOM CUPBOARD
SOME HOPES!

PIGGY OUGHT TO BE PLEASED TO KNOW WE'RE ALL ENJOYING HIS SPLENDID COOKING. HEE-HEE!

The MONKS and the
GEORDIES
In a great tale of Flying Saucers—and flying fists!

A FLYING SAUCER HAS BEEN SIGHTED IN THE HIGH STREET!
WHAT?

COME ON! WE'LL SHOW YOU!
BETTER HAVE YOUR BATON AT THE READY, CONSTABLE!
RIGHT, SARGE!

CINEMA
NOW SHOWING
SPACE WARS
THERE IT IS! HO-HO!

CINEMA
NOW SHOW
PACE WAR
YOU CHEEKY, YOUNG RASCALS. THAT'S ENOUGH OF YOUR TALL TALES!

JINGS! THIS IS A BRAW FILM, ISN'T IT?

On the way home—
DO YOU THINK THERE REALLY ARE SUCH THINGS AS FLYING SAUCERS, BIG JOCK?
COURSE THERE ARE, AND WE'LL DO SOME FLYING SAUCER SPOTTING ON THE COMMON TONIGHT.
OHO! I MUST TELL MY GEORDIE PALS ABOUT THIS.

Back at the Geordies' hut—
IS THAT SO? THEN WE'LL MAKE SURE THEY SEE A FLYING SAUCER TONIGHT, LADS!
HA-HA! WE'LL SOON HAVE OUR MASTERPIECE FINISHED.
SNIP! SNIP!
PASTE
That night—
SPOT ANYTHING, ECK?
NOT A THING— EXCEPT A GEORDIE RUNNING THIS WAY!
I CLAIM FIRST THUMP AT HIM!
WHEEZE! WAIT, JOCKS! I'D RATHER BE WITH YOU THAN NEAR THAT THING IN THE FIELD!
WHAT THING? TELL US—OR WE'LL BIFF YOU!
A FLYING SAUCER, THAT'S WHAT. ON THE COMMON!
WE'RE NOT FRIGHTENED OF IT. COME ON, JOCKS!
THAT NEWS ABOUT THE FLYING SAUCER HAS SAVED YOU FROM A BASHING, GEORDIE!
IT-IT'S A BIT S-SPOOKY OUT HERE, B-BIG JOCK!
N-NO SIGN OF THE S-SAUCER. ER, LET'S G-GO HOME THEN!
STAY HERE, JOCKS! IF WE SPOT IT, WE'LL BECOME FAMOUS, REMEMBER!

RIGHT, LADS! MOVE FORWARD NOW. THE GLOW-IN-THE-DARK PAINT WILL ATTRACT THE ATTENTION OF THE JOCKS.
CAPERING COMETS! LOOK! THERE IT IS OVER THERE, LIKE A GIANT LUMINOUS HAGGIS. AND IT'S HOVERING!
HELP!
YAHOO!
DIVE!
AND I'M HIDING!
GET CLOSER AND START MAKING NOTES ABOUT IT, YOU COWARDS!
NO, BIG JOCK! I'M NOT FEELING WELL ENOUGH TO WRITE NOTES!
IT COULD BE FULL OF GREEN MONSTERS!
PUSH!
THE JOCKS ARE COMING CLOSER. GET YOUR TORCHES READY, LADS!

EEK! DEATH RAYS! RUN!
WAAH!
HELP!

Next day—
—AND THEN THEY TURNED THEIR DEATH RAYS ON US AND WE JUST GOT AWAY IN TIME!
QUITE A STORY, BUT YOU NEED PROOF—A PHOTO OR A PIECE OF THE SAUCER!

TEACHER'S RIGHT! WE NEED PROOF. WE'LL GO BACK TO THE COMMON TONIGHT!
GULP! WE WILL?

After school—
GO HOME AND FETCH YOUR CAMERA, ECK.
OH, ALL RIGHT, BUT I STILL DON'T LIKE THE IDEA!

On the way to the Jocks' hut—
THEATRE
WE'LL BORROW THESE SPACEMEN COSTUMES FOR TONIGHT, AND PUT THE WIND UP THE JOCKS AGAIN!
GOSH! SO IT WAS THE GEORDIES! I'LL HAVE TO TELL BIG JOCK THAT WE'VE BEEN TRICKED!

OKAY, JOCKS! WE'LL SURPRISE THOSE GEORDIE ROTTERS IN OUR OWN SPACEMEN COSTUMES AND THEY'RE THE ONES WHO'LL BE FRIGHTENED! GET BUSY, JOCKS!

Soon—
I FOUND THIS BOX OF OLD COLOURED ELECTRIC BULBS. WE CAN USE THEM FOR EYES!
WE CAN CUT THIS HOSE UP FOR SNOUTS.
Meanwhile—
MY BOYS ARE ALL TALKING ABOUT A FLYING SAUCER THEY SAW ON THE COMMON.
STRANGE! SO ARE MINE. I THINK WE SHOULD TAKE A LOOK ALONG, JUST IN CASE IT'S TRUE!
That night—
IT'S TIME FOR US TO SET OFF, JOCKS.
I HEAR STRANGE VOICES UP AHEAD, TEACHER.
GULP! I HOPE YOU ARE MISTAKEN.
GASP! LOOK AT THAT! WE'VE BEEN INVADED BY CREATURES FROM OUTER SPACE!
EEK! THEY APPEAR TO BE CALLING TO EACH OTHER IN SOME SORT OF MUMBO-JUMBO, BUT I CAN'T MAKE OUT WHAT THEY'RE SAYING.

SQUEAL!
GRUNT!
SHRIEK!
THERE ARE WEIRD SPACEMEN ON THE COMMON!
WHAT?
IT'S HORRIBLE! RUN FOR THE POLICE STATION— QUICK!
MOAN! THAT TAUGHT THEM A LESSON! OOH! MY JAW!
BET THOSE JOCKS ARE SEEING STARS. GROAN!
WHOA! LOOK AT THIS—IT'S STUFF LEFT BEHIND BY THE JOCKS AND GEORDIES IF YOU ASK ME!
SCREECH!

Later—
YOU'RE BEING CHARGED WITH GIVING FALSE INFORMATION. YOU SHOULD BE ASHAMED OF YOURSELVES! NO WONDER YOUR PUPILS TELL TALL TALES.
BUT—BUT WE DID SEE THEM!
OH, DEAR! THIS WILL GET INTO THE PAPERS!
THIS PRANK HAS MADE THESE TEACHERS A LAUGHING STOCK!
GURR! IT WAS ALL THE GEORDIES' FAULT! BASH THEM!
SNORT! OUR TEACHERS WILL BLAME US FOR THIS WHEN IT WAS REALLY THE JOCKS' FAULT!
DAILY GOSSIP
HOAX BY TEACHERS
DAILY WAIL
TEACHERS CHARGED
YAHOO!
HO-HO! THAT'S ONE JOCK GONE INTO ORBIT!
OUCH!
OOF!
AND THERE'S A GEORDIE SEEING STARS!

THE TRICKS OF
SCREWY DRIVER
GOSH! IT'S SNOWING HARD. HOW WILL I GET TO WORK TOMORROW?
LEAVE THAT TO ME, DAD!
I'LL NEED THE ENGINE FROM THE MOTOR MOWER...
Next day—
COME ON, DAD! I'VE MADE A MOTOR SLEDGE. I'LL START UP BEFORE YOU CLIMB ABOARD.
YEEAGH! IT'S SHOWERING ME WITH SNOW! STOP IT, SCREWY!
EH?
WHOOSH!
BAH! YOU'D BETTER DESIGN A SAFER MACHINE—AND HURRY UP WITH IT!
YES, DAD!
GET A MOVE ON, SCREWY! I'M GOING TO BE LATE!
NEARLY READY!
THERE! INSTEAD OF A PADDLE, IT'S GOT A PROPELLER NOW.
STILL DOESN'T LOOK SAFE TO ME!
OOPS! I'VE HIT THE EDGE OF A SNOWY BANK!
AARGH! WE'RE BEING THROWN OFF!
HELP!

How do you start a toys' race?—READY, TEDDY, GO!

Desperate DAWG
HEY! YOU'RE SUPPOSED TO BE KEEPING THE PEACE WHILE THE SHERIFF'S AWAY, DESPERATE DAWG. IT'S YOUR JOB TO SILENCE THESE ROWDIES!
ANG!
BANG!
YIPPEE!
I HAVE AN IDEA—BUT I'LL HAVE TO BORROW THE TOWN HALL BELL FOR IT.
TOWN HALL
BANG! BANG! BANG! BANG!
YOO-HA!
HOI! WHAT'S GOING ON?
BONG! BONG!
YOW!
AAGH!
HA-HA! THAT SHOULD TEACH 'EM THAT SILENCE IS GOLDEN!
RRRRRING!
NOW I'LL TAKE THIS BACK TO THE TOWN HALL.
DAGNAB IT! IT'S CAUGHT ON TO SOMETHING.
CRACK!
BONG!

HELP! MY BULLS ARE ESCAPING!
STAMPEDE! STAMPEDE!
I'LL NEED THE BACK OF THIS TRUCK.
RUN!
GOOD-OH! THEY'VE RUN RIGHT ROUND THE BLOCK.
HELP!
GOT YOU!
PLONK!
OKAY, ALL YOUR BULLS ARE SAFELY BACK IN THE TRUCK.
!
TEE-HEE! WHAT A GUY THAT DESPERATE DAWG IS!
AND WHAT'S MORE, IT DOESN'T MATTER ABOUT THE BUSTED TAIL-BOARD. THOSE STEERS CAN'T RUN AWAY NOW!
GASP!

KORKY the CAT
GRAND CHRISTMAS FETE
WHAT CAN YOU DO AT THE FETE, KORKY?
I CAN PUT ON A JUGGLING DISPLAY WITH PLATES.
LIKE SO—
NOT BAD!
OH, NO!
CRASH
CRASH
YOU'D BETTER SWEEP UP THE MESS, THEN GO AND HELP IN THE TEA-TENT INSTEAD.
In the tea-tent—
CARRY THESE DISHES OFF FOR WASHING, KORKY—AND BE CAREFUL!
YES, LADY!
TEAS
WOW!
CRASH
AARGH!
SLIP
The fete boss arrives—
WELL, HE CERTAINLY MAKES A GOOD JOB OF SWEEPING UP BROKEN CROCKERY!
YES, YOU'RE AN EXPERT AT USING A BRUSH AND SHOVEL, KORKY. COME WITH ME—I'VE GOT JUST THE JOB FOR YOU!

SMASH the CROCKERY
SMASH
SMASH
SMASH
SUFFERING SAUCERS! LOOK WHAT THEY'VE SENT ME TO DO— SWEEP UP AT THE CROCKERY SMASHING STALL. I'M GOING TO ASK FOR DANGER MONEY AS WELL!
3 BALLS FOR 10P

PETER'S POCKET Grandpa

WHEEZE! PANT! I'M OUT OF BREATH. IT'S HARD WORK SKATING AT MY AGE!
HEY! THOSE BOYS' KITES GIVE ME A GREAT IDEA!
THE KITE YOU MADE FOR ME IS CATCHING THE WIND, PETER! NOW TO TEST OUT MY IDEA.
I HOPE YOU CAN STEER WITH THOSE GUIDE ROPES, GRANDPA.
SWERVE!
WHOOPS! OFF I GO!
LOOK HOW WELL I CAN CORNER, PETER!
NO MORE WALKING AROUND FOR ME! IT'S TOO SLOW. AS LONG AS THERE'S A BREEZE, I CAN GO LIKE THE WIND ON SKATES. HURRAY!
ZOOOM!

JEWE
PTL 742N
OH, DEAR! MY KITE HAS GOT TANGLED IN THE DOOR OF THAT PARKED VAN.
JUMP INTO THE VAN, SYD. GET GOING, DRIVER!
PTL 742N
GASP! I'M ROLLING RIGHT UNDER THE VAN! HEY! WHAT'S GOING ON?
SLAM!
ROBBERS! AND MY KITE IS CAUGHT FAST. I'M BEING TOWED ALONG ON THE GETAWAY!
PTL 742N
EEK! I MUST BE DOING FIFTY MILES AN HOUR!
SCREECH!
A SHARP BEND! I'M FLYING NOW!
L 742N
WHIPPP
XSP
I'VE LANDED—BUT RIGHT IN THE PATH OF THAT LORRY! AARGH!

PHEW! JUST MISSED ME!
SWERVE
PTL
AH! SLOWING DOWN AT LAST! THEY MUST BE NEAR THEIR HIDEOUT. I'LL MAKE 'EM PAY FOR THIS!
SLAM!
WE'RE HERE! THE COPS WON'T FIND US NOW.
I'M FREE OF THE VAN NOW, BUT HOW CAN I GET HELP TO CAPTURE THESE ROBBERS?
AHA! SOME OF THIS GEAR SHOULD BE USEFUL. I'LL GET BUSY AT ONCE.
I'LL DRAG THE ROPE ALL THE WAY ROUND THE HUT. OH, CRUMBS! IT'S GETTING HEAVIER ALL THE TIME!
NEARLY THERE! JUST A FEW INCHES MORE. HEAVE!

I'VE TIED A SLIP KNOT IN IT. NOW I NEED THIS END OF THE ROPE.
THAT'S THE SHED MADE FAST TO THE TRACTOR. NOW FOR THE NEXT PART OF MY PLAN.
HOW'S THIS FOR A DISTRESS SIGNAL PAINTED ON AN OLD SACK?
SOS
NOW FOR A DIFFICULT CLIMB UP THE TRACTOR'S TYRE. GASP! PUFF!
UP COMES MY DISTRESS FLAG.
SOS
SOS
THAT'S GREAT! IT'S FLUTTERING NICELY IN THE BREEZE.

I'VE TURNED ON THE IGNITION KEY. LET'S HOPE THE STARTER KNOB ISN'T TOO STIFF . . .
BRRRM!
STARTED FIRST TIME! NOW TO SET HER ROLLING.
SOS
BRRMM!
DB 104
HOI! WHAT'S GOING ON OUT THERE?
SHUDDER!
PING!
PING!
CREAK!
AARGH! HELP! THE HUT IS FALLING TO BITS! STOP!

ERK! A DRIVERLESS TRACTOR FLYING AN S.O.S. SIGNAL. WHERE DID THAT COME FROM?
SMASH!
SOS
THUD!
CYCLE PATROL TO H.Q. I'M NOT SURE WHAT'S GOING ON HERE, BUT SEND SOME OFFICERS AT ONCE!
GROAN!
WHAT HAPPENED? THERE MUST HAVE BEEN AN EARTHQUAKE!
THOSE GUYS GROANING IN THERE, CONSTABLE. THEY'RE THE CROOKS WHO ROBBED THE HIGH STREET JEWELLER'S AN HOUR AGO!
GOSH!

THEY'RE ONLY SHAKEN UP, BUT THEY'LL NEED A LONG REST IN JAIL. ER—COULD I CADGE A LIFT HOME?
WELL, CERTAINLY! I RECKON YOU DESERVE IT!
CRUMBS, GRANDPA! ALL THAT HAPPENED JUST BECAUSE YOU WANTED TO TAKE THE HARD WORK OUT OF ROLLER SKATING!
Daily Globe
MIDGET MAN BAGS TWO CROOKS!
CHUCKLE! AND I GOT A NICE REWARD, PETER! I EXPECT YOU'LL HELP ME TO BLOW THAT TOMORROW, EH?

IZZY SKINT
HE ALWAYS IS!
IT'S NICE OF YOU TO CARRY MY SHOPPING BAG FOR ME, IZZY.
IT'S A PLEASURE, MRS BINKS.
HERE'S TWENTY PENCE FOR HELPING ME, IZZY.
THANK YOU.
OH, BOY! I WAS SKINT, BUT NOW I'VE GOT TWENTY PENCE. THAT'S NOT TO BE SNEEZED AT!
YOU DID HAVE TWENTY PENCE, IZZY!
BUT NOT NOW!
SNATCH!
YOU'RE RIGHT, TWENTY PENCE ISN'T TO BE SNEEZED AT! HEE-HEE!
BAH! THE ROTTERS!
GOSH! MRS JONES HAS DROPPED SOMETHING FROM HER SHOPPING BASKET!
BUS STOP
MRS JONES!
TOO LATE—SHE'S GONE!
BUS STOP
I KNOW WHERE MRS JONES LIVES. SHE'S BOUND TO REWARD ME FOR RETURNING THIS.
PARK

YOU'RE SO KIND, IZZY! THANKS FOR HANDING ME THIS PARCEL.
HEY! GIVE IT BACK TO ME. IT'S NOT MINE!
YEAH! IT'S OURS NOW. CATCH, BILL!
OVER TO YOU, DAVE!
TA!
CRUMBS!
KICK!
NO, DON'T! STOP!
PLOP!
PHOOF!
HO-HO! THE BAG WAS FULL OF PEPPER!
AH-CHOO! AH-CHOO!
AH-CHOO! AH-CHOO!
HELP! ATISHOO!
ATISHOO!
GURR! COME BACK! A-CHOO!
THAT BAG OF PEPPER WAS DEFINITELY TO BE SNEEZED AT! HEE-HEE!

PUZZLE ANSWERS

A SUPER "ICE" SCREAM! SEE PAGES 34—35

1—Slicer, 2—Mice, 3—Notice, 4—Liquorice, 5—Office, 6—Spice, 7—Crevice, 8—Juice, 9—Dice, 10—Policeman, 11—Biceps, 12—Vice, 13—Choice, 14—Venice, 15—Officers, 16—Rice, 17—Voice, 18—Plaice, 19—Advice, 20—Price, 21—Practice, 22—Apprentice, 23—Iceberg.

SPOT THE "OWL"! SEE PAGES 98—99

1—Prowler, 2—Blowlamp, 3—Windowledge, 4—Barrowload, 5—Slowly, 6—Bowler, 7—Lowlands, 8—Scowl, 9—Towline, 10—Bowl, 11—Yowl, 12—Bowlegged, 13—Howl, 14—Fowl, 15—Bowler, 16—Bowls, 17—Narrowly, 18—Howler, 19—Knowledge, 20—Growl.

HE TOSSED HIS PANCAKE MIGHTY HIGH!
AND I SEE NOW WHERE HE'S GONNA GET THE MEAT!